Sing with Young Life

FOR GROUP SINGING!
You don't have any music to read, so just let go and sing!

MUSIC ACCOMPANIMENT BOOK ALSO AVAILABLE

Typesetting, Cindy Johnson Merkle
Layout, Marsha Ricketts
Photos: Dan Stearns, Rudy Vetter, Paul Rey

MEMBER OF
EVANGELICAL CHRISTIAN
PUBLISHERS ASSOCIATION

Printed in U.S.A.

Published by Young Life, Colorado Springs, CO 80901

More than thirty-five years of experiment and experience have helped Young Life build effective ways to communicate, and SING has emerged as a major tool.

Each week during school some 70,000 young people are involved in 1100 Young Life clubs nationwide. A club is an informal session, usually in the home of one of the kids. They come together for fun, fellowship, singing and words from the leader in comfortable, everday language about Jesus Christ and His reality today.

A Young Life staff man or woman, or a qualified volunteer, leads the club. Staff people are well trained seminary graduates, or have a Masters Degree in Youth Ministries. All volunteers work under the supervision of professional staff. Young Life's nationwide staff includes 650 full and part-time leaders. Five thousand volunteers lead clubs or assist the staff.

Songs are selected by Young Life field staff with the special help of Joni Sheffer and Alison Lammott.

Grateful acknowledgment is made of the cooperation of all the individuals and publishers who have given permission for the use of original and copyrighted material in this collection. We have tried to locate the copyright owner and secure proper permission for each song in SING WITH YOUNG LIFE; any error or omission is unintentional and we shall be glad to make necessary correction in a later printing.

MORNING HAS BROKEN 1

Words by Eleanor Farjeon
Gaelic Melody

C Am Dm G F C
1. Morning has broken like the first morning,
Em Am Em F G
Blackbird has spoken like the first bird.
C F C F Dm
Praise for the singing, praise for the morning,
G C F G C
Praise for them, springing fresh from the Word!

2. Sweet the rain's new fall, sunlit from heaven,
Like the first dewfall on the first grass.
Praise for the sweetness of the wet garden,
Sprung in completeness where His feet pass.

3. Mine is the sunlight, mine is the morning,
Born of the one light Eden saw play.
Praise with elation, praise ev'ry morning —
God's recreation of the new day.

2 BYE BYE, LOVE

Words by Felice Bryant and
Boudleaux Bryant

Chorus:

B♭ F
Bye Bye, Love:
B♭ F
Bye bye, happiness;
B♭ F C^7 F
Hello loneliness I think I'm gonna cry;
B♭ F
Bye Bye Love;
B♭ F
Bye bye, sweet caress;
B♭ F C F
Hello emptiness; I feel like I could die;
C^7 F
Bye bye, my love, bye bye.

C^7 F
1. There goes my baby with someone new;
C^7 F
She sure looks happy; I sure am blue;
F^7 B♭ B C^7
She was my baby till he stepped in;
F
Good-bye to romance that might have been;

(Chorus)

2. I'm through with romance, I'm through with love
I'm through with counting the stars above;
And here's the reason that I'm so free;
My lovin' baby is through with me;

(Chorus)

SING HALLELUJAH! 3

Words and Music by Orien Johnson

Em B7
There's a word of exultation, full of joy and inspiration,
Em B7 Em
Echo now to all creation, sing Hallelujah, sing!
Em B7
'Tis a word of adoration to the God of our salvation,
Em B7 Em
Sing to every tribe and nation, sing Hallelujah, sing!
Em
Sing Hallelujah, Sing Hallelujah,
B7
Sing Hallelujah, Sing Hallelujah,
Em
Sing Hallelujah, Sing Hallelujah,
B7 Em
Sing, Halleujah, sing!
Em
Sing Hallelujah, Sing Hallelujah,
B7
Sing Hallelujah, Sing Hallelujah,
Em
Sing Hallelujah, Sing Hallelujah,
B7 Em
Sing Hallelujah, sing!

4 CIRCLES

Words and Music by Harry Chapin

C Cmaj7 C6 Cmaj7 C Cmaj7 Dm7
All my life's a circle, sunrise and sundown;
Dm Dm7 Dm6 G7
the moon rolls through the nighttime
C Cmaj7 C6 Cmaj7
till the daybreak comes around.
C Cmaj7 C6 Cmaj7 C Cmaj7 Dm7
All my life's a circle but I can't tell you why;
G7 F G7 C Cmaj7
the season's spinin' round again, the years keep rollin' by.

C Cmaj7 C6 Cmaj7 C
It seems like I've been here before,
Cmaj7 Dm7
I can't remember when,
Dm Dm7 Dm6 G7 C Cmaj7 C6 Cmaj7
but I got this funny feelin' that I'll be back once again.
C Cmaj7 C6 Cmaj7
There's no straight lines make up my life
C Cmaj7 Dm7
and all my roads have bends,
G7 F G7 C (Cmaj7 C6 Cmaj7)
there's no clearcut beginnin's and so far no dead-ends.

I've found you a thousand times,
I guess you've done the same,
but then we lose each other,
it's just like a children's game.
But as I see you here again
the thought runs through my mind,
our love is like a circle, let's go round one more time.

(fade)

I AM NOT SKILLED TO UNDERSTAND 5

By Dora Greenwell and William J. Kirkpatrick

(Capo 2)

D A^7
1. I am not skilled to understand
D A A^7 D
What God hath will'd, what God hath plann'd;
A^7 D G
I only know at His right hand
D A A^7 D
Stands One who is my Savior.

2. I take Him at His word indeed
"Christ died for sinners," this I read;
And in my heart I find a need
Of Him to be my Savior.

3. And was there then no other way
For God to take? I cannot say;
I only bless Him, day by day,
Who saved me thro' my Savior.

4. That He should leave His place on high,
And come for sinful man to die,
You count it strange? So once did I,
Before I knew my Savior.

5. And oh, that He fulfilled may see
The travail of His soul in me,
And with His work contented be,
As I with my dear Savior.

6. Yes, living, dying, let me bring
My strength, my solace from this spring,
That He who lives to be my King
Once died to be my Savior.

6 EARLY IN THE MORNING

By Paul Stookey

1. C F C
Well early in the mornin' 'bout the break of day,
C E^m F G
I asked the Lord help me find the way,
C F C F C
Help me find the way to the promised land.
F A^m D^7
This lonely body needs a helping hand,
A^m C C A^m E^m
I asked the Lord to help me please,
F^7 F C F C
Find the way.

2. When the new day is a dawning bow my head in pray'r,
I pray to the Lord won't you lead me there?
Won't you guide me safely to the golden stair?
Won't you let this body your burden share?
I pray to the Lord won't you lead me please,
Lead me there?

3. When the judgment comes to find the world in shame,
When the trumpet blows won't you call my name?
When the thunder rolls and the heavens rain,
When the sun turns black, never shine again,
When the trumpet blows won't you call me please,
Call my name?

BAMBOO

By Dave Van Ronk

G
1. You take a stick of bamboo,
F
You take a stick of bamboo,
G F
You take a stick of bamboo, you throw it in the water,
G F G
Oh — Oh — Hannah!
G
You take a stick of bamboo,
F
You take a stick of bamboo,
G F
You take a stick of bamboo, you throw it in the water,
G F G
Oh — Oh — Hannah!
G F G F G
River — She come down — River — She come down.

2. You travel on the river, You travel on the river,
You travel on the river, You travel on the water,
Oh — Oh — Hannah!
You travel on the river, You travel on the river,
You travel on the river, You travel on the water,
Oh — Oh — Hannah!
River — She come down — River — She come down.

3. My home's across the river, My home's across the river,
My home's across the river,
My home's across the water,
Oh — Oh — Hannah!
My home's across the river, My home's across the river,
My home's across the river,
My home's across the water,
Oh — Oh — Hannah!
River — She come down — River — She come down.
G
You take a stick of bamboo,
F
You take a stick of bamboo,
G F
You take a stick of bamboo, you throw it in the water.

8 SEEK YE FIRST

By Karen Lafferty

```
        C          G        Am            Em
1.      Seek ye first the kingdom of God
        Dm7        C        G    G7
        And His righteousness,
          C                  G                  Am            Em
        And all these things shall be added unto you,
        Dm7   C       Dm7/G C
        Al-le-lu, Al-le-lu-ia
        C  G  Am Em Dm7 C G G7 C G Am Em Dm7/C Dm7/G C
        Al-le-lu-ia, Al-le-lu-ia, Al-le-lu-ia, Al-le-lu-ia.

2.      Ask, and it shall be given unto you.
        Seek, and ye shall find.
        Knock, and it shall be opened unto you.
        Al-le-lu, Al-le-lu-ia
        Al-le-lu-ia, Al-le-lu-ia, Al-le-lu-ia, Al-le-lu-ia.
```

"The second verse is not part of the song as originally written. Its origin is unknown."

9 FATHER I ADORE YOU

By Terrye Coelho

```
        D Em        A    D
1.      Father I adore You,
        D         Em     A    D
        Lay my life before You,
          D Em A    D
        How I love You.

2.      Jesus I adore You,
        Lay my life before You,
        How I love You.

3.      Spirit I adore You,
        Lay my life before You,
        How I love You.
```

THE NEW 23rd

Words and Music by Ralph Carmichael

C F
Because the Lord is my shepherd
G C
I have ev'rything that I need.
F C F
He lets me rest in meadows green
C G7 C
And leads me beside the quiet stream.
F C F
He keeps on giving life to me
C G7 C
And helps me to do what honors Him the most.
Am Am7 Fmaj7
Even when walking thru the dark valley of death,
Em
Valley of death,
Am G Am D G F Em G7
I will never be afraid, for He is close beside me.
C F G C
Guarding, guiding all the way, He spreads a feast before me
F C F
In the presence of my enemies
C G7 C
He welcomes me as His special guest
C A
With blessing overflowing,
D Dm E
His goodness and unfailing kindness
Am E Am
Shall be with me all of my life.
D Dm G7 C G7 C A♭ Gsus Dm F
And afterwards I shall live with Him forever, forever —
C F C
In His home, forever in His home.
F C
Forever in His home.

11 HIS SHEEP AM I

By Orien Johnson

VERSE:

C G
In God's green pastures feeding, by His cool waters lie;
G^7 C G^7
Soft, in the evening walk my Lord and I.
C F
All the sheep of His pastures fare so wondrously fine . . .
C G^7 C
His sheep am I.

CHORUS:

C F
Girls: Waters cool *Guys:* (in the valley,)
G
Girls: pastures green, *Guys:* (on the mountain,)
G^7
Girls: In the eve ––– *Guys:* In the evening
C
Together: Walk my Lord and I.
F
Girls: Dark the night, *Guys:* (in the valley,)
C
Girls: Rough the way, *Guys:* (on the mountain,)
G^7
Girls: Step by step *Guys:* Step by step
C
Together: My Lord and I.

(Repeat verse)

MY SWEET LADY

By John Denver

Chorus:

F G C C7
Close your eyes and rest your weary mind.
F G C C7
I promise I will stay right here beside you.
F G C
Today our lives were joined, became entwined.
Am Am7 Dm G
I wish that you could know how much I love you.

Cmaj7 Dm/A C Cmaj7 F/C
1. Lady, are your crying, do the tears belong to me?
Fm C Cmaj7 C9 Cmaj7 Dm G
Did you think our time together was all gone?
Cmaj7 Dm/C C Cmaj7 F/C
Lady, you've been dreaming I'm as close as I can be
Fm Cmaj7 Dm G C C7
and I swear to you our time has just begun.

(Chorus)

2. Lady, are you happy, do you feel the way I do,
Are there meanings that you've never seen before?
Lady, my sweet lady I just can't believe it's true
And it's like I've never ever loved before.

(Chorus)

3. Lady, are you crying, do the tears belong to me?
Did you think our time together was all gone?
Lady, my sweet lady I'm as close as I can be
And I swear to you our time has just begun.

13 FAIREST LORD JESUS

From the German 17th Century
Silesian Folk Song

Arr. by James Hopkirk

D B^m E^m A D B^m E^m A D
1. **Fairest Lord Jesus, Ruler of all nature,**
G D G D G F^m A^7
O Thou of God and man the Son;
F^m B^m D F^m G A A^7 D
Thee will I cherish, Thee will I honor,
B^m F^m E^m D A^7 D
Thou my soul's glory, joy, and crown.

2. **Fair are the meadows, Fairer still the woodlands,**
Robed in the blooming garb of spring;
Jesus is fairer, Jesus is purer,
Who makes the woeful heart to sing.

3. **Fair is the sunshine, Fairer still the moonlight,**
And fair the twinkling, starry host;
Jesus shines brighter, Jesus shines purer,
Than all the angels heaven can boast.

4. **All fairest beauty Heavenly and earthly,**
Wondrously Jesus, is found in Thee;
None can be nearer, fairer or dearer,
Than Thou, my Saviour, art to me.

14 I BELIEVE IN MUSIC

Words and Music by Mac Davis

F G^m
1. **Well I could just sit around makin' music all day long.**
C^7
Long as I'm makin' music
F
I know I can't do nobody wrong.

B♭ F
And who knows, maybe someday
Gm
I'll come up with a song,
C
That makes people wanna stop their fussin' and fightin'

Just long enough to sing along. —
F
(Ev'rybody sing)
F Gm B♭ C F
I believe in music. I believe in love.
F Gm B♭ C F
I believe in music. I believe in love.

2. Music is love, love is music if you know what I mean.
People who believe in music
are the happiest people I ever seen.
So clap your hands, stomp your feet —
shake your tambourine
Lift your voices to the sky,
God loves you when you sing,
I believe in music. I believe in love.
F Gm
Sing it to me children, I believe in music
B C F
Lord, knows that I believe in love.

3. Music is the universal language and love is the key
To brotherhood and peace and understanding
to living in harmony.
So take your brother by the hand
and sing along with me,
And find out what it really means
to be young and rich and free.
I believe in music, I believe in love.
Sing it to me children, I believe in music
Lord, knows that I believe in love.

15 WEAVE ME THE SUNSHINE

Words and Music by Peter Yarrow

Chorus:

```
 Dm7    G7      C             Am7      F             G    C
Weave, weave, weave me the sunshine out of the falling rain.
                 Am7
(Out of the falling –––)
 Dm7               G7         C      Am7
Weave me the hope of a new tomorrow
     D       D7    G
and fill my cup again.
```

and fill my cup again. *(sing twice between verses)*

A^m E

1. Well, I've seen the steel and the concrete crumble,

F G C

Shine on me again.

A^m A^{m7} D^7

The proud and the mighty all have stumbled,

G G^7

Shine on me again, now.

(Chorus)

2. They say that the tree of loving,
Shine on me again,
Grows on the bank of the river of suffering,
Shine on me again.

(Chorus)

3. If only I could heal your sorrow,
Shine on me again,
I'd help you to find your new tomorrow,
Shine on me again.

(Chorus)

4. Well I've seen the steel and the concrete crumble,
Shine on me again,
The proud and the mighty all have stumbled,
Shine on me again, now.

(Chorus)

5. Only you can climb that mountain,
Shine on me again.
If you want to drink in the golden fountain,
Shine on me again.
(Sing it out now.)

(Chorus)

16 IN HIS NAME

By Bob McCook

Chorus:

C Em F G
You and I can climb every mountain
C Em
Cross every stream
F G
And drink from every fountain
C Em
In His Na - - - - - me
F G C (Em F G)
In His Name In His Name.

Am
1. Truth is gone,
Em
the world proclaims
F G
No foundation now remains.
Am Em
Yesterday can not return
F G7
Tomorrow won't be the same

But . . . .

(Chorus)

2. Men hide their deeds,
From human eyes
Their hope in self alone
Man's power fails,
The light grows dim,
Blind lead blind, I hear them wail.
But . . . .

(Chorus)

LET SOMETHING GOOD BE SAID 17

Words and Music by Sam Johnson

Chorus:

G C G D D^7 G
And so I charge thee by the thorny crown
C G D D^7 G
and by the Cross on which the Savior bled
C G D D^7 G
and by your own soul's hope for fair renown
C D^7 G
Let something good be said.

C G
1. Come listen to me if your time allows.
C D
We have a plea that must at last be heard.
G D G
Speak out the truth, and speak it long and loud.
C D
And measure e-ve-r-y word.

2. The tongue is mighty let its words be true.
We have a message, we are told to tell.
We've made mistakes, but we're just passing through.
We haven't done too well.

3. All my possessions I will gladly share.
(It's almost over with these flesh and bones.)
I do not need them for my journey here
Or for my journey home.

4. Now is the time a new song must be sung.
We're born in freedom
And must not be shackled down.
It's plain to see, God made us to be free
And wear an open crown.

BLOWIN' IN THE WIND

Words and Music by Bob Dylan

Chorus:

```
    G               A        D      F♯         Bm
The answer my friend is blowin' in the wind,
    G            A             D
the answer is blowin' in the wind.
```

```
          D              G            D
1.    How many roads must a man walk down
                 G              Asus4 A
      before you call him a man?
                D            G               D
      Yes, 'n' how many seas must a white dove sail
                      G          Asus4 A
      before she sleeps in the sand?
                D            G                  D
      Yes, 'n' how many times must the cannon balls fly
                        G          Asus4 A
      before they're forever banned?
```

2. How many times must a man look up
before he can see the sky?
Yes, 'n' how many ears must one man have
before he can hear people cry?
Yes, 'n' how many deaths will it take till he knows
that too many people have died?

3. How many years can a mountain exist
before it's washed to the sea?
Yes, 'n' how many years can some people exist
before they're allowed to be free?
Yes, 'n' how many times can a man turn his head
pretending he just doesn't see?

PRAISE THE SAVIOR, YE WHO KNOW HIM! 19

Traditional German Melody

By Thomas Kelly

(Capo 1) D7 G D
1. Praise the Savior, ye who know Him!
G D G Am D
Who can tell how much we owe Him?
G C
Gladly let us render to Him
Am G D7 G
All we are and have.

2. Jesus is the name that charms us;
He for conflict fits and arms us;
Nothing moves and nothing harms us
While we trust in Him.

3. Trust in Him, ye saints, forever;
He is faithful, changing never;
Neither force nor guile can sever
Those He loves from Him.

4. Keep us, Lord, O keep us cleaving
To Thyself and still believing;
Till the hour of our receiving,
Promised joys with Thee.

5. Then we shall be where we would be,
Then we shall be what we should be;
Things that are not now, nor could be,
Soon shall be our own.

BABYLON 20

Adaptation and Arrangement by
Don McLean and Lee Hays

Am F Am
By the waters, the waters of Babylon,
E Am
We lay down and wept, and wept for thee, Zion.
Am Dm Am E Am
We remember thee, remember thee, remember thee, Zion.

21 THANK YOU LORD

Words and Music by Dan Burgess

Cmaj7 D7 Bm7 E7
1. Thank you Lord for the trials that come my way,
Em7 Am7 D7 G
in that way I can grow each day as I let you lead.
Cmaj7
And thank you, Lord,
D7 Bm7
for the patience those trials bring,
E7 Em7 Am7 D7 G
in that process of growing I can learn to care.
F6 Cmaj7 D7
But it goes against the way I am
Bm7 Em7
to put my human nature down,
Am7 D7 G
and let the Spirit take control of all I do
F6 Cmaj7
'cause when those trials come,
D7 Bm7 Em7
and let the Spirit take control of all I do —
Am7 D7 G Gmaj9
and God's soft prompting can be easily ignored.

2. I thank you Lord with each trial I feel inside,
that you're there to help lead
And guide me away from wrong.
'cause you promised, Lord, that with ev'ry testing
that your way of escaping is easier to bear.
But it goes against the way I am
to put my human nature down,
and let the Spirit take control of all I do —
'cause when those trials come,
my human nature shouts the thing to do;
and God's soft prompting can be easily ignored.

Cmaj7 D7 Bm7 E7
3. **I thank you Lord, for the victory that growing brings,**
Em7 Am7 D7 G Gmaj9
In surrender of ev'rything life is so worthwhile.
Cmaj7
And I thank you Lord
D7 Bm7
that when ev'rything's put in place,
Em7 Am7
Out in front I can see your face
D7 G A7 Am7 G
and it's there you belong.

22 HUMBLE THYSELF

(unknown)

Dm Am Dm
Guys: **Humble thyself in the sight of the Lord.**

Dm Am Dm
Gals: *Humble thyself in the sight of the Lord.*

Dm Am Dm
Guys: **Humble thyself in the sight of the Lord.**

Dm Am Dm
Gals: *Humble thyself in the sight of the Lord.*

Dm C Dm
Guys: **And He . . . shall lift . . . you up.**

Gals: *. . . . .And He . . . shall lift you up.*

Dm C Dm
Guys: **And He . . . shall lift . . . you up.**

Gals: *. . . . And He . . . shall lift you up.*

BLINDMAN

Traditional

Arr. by Yohann Anderson

```
 Am       G                    F        E
Blindman stood on the way and cried;
 Am       G                    F        E
Blindman stood on the way and cried;
 Am       G                    F        E          E7
Blindman stood on the way and cried; sayin' Oh
                 Am G F  E7            Am G F
show me the way — Show me the way —
 E7             Am G F        E          E7
Show me the way,     the way to go home.
```

2. Jesus stood by the road and cried,
Jesus stood by the road and cried;
Jesus stood by the road and cried; sayin' Oh
I am the Truth
I am the Light
I am the way, the way to go home.

I NEED THE LORD TO HELP ME

Traditional

```
              D
1.    At a time like this
          D
      at a time like this
          D    G   D
      at a time like this
       G D              A7    D
      Oh I need the Lord to help me.
```

2. On a day like this

3. At a time like this

4. When I'm down and out

25 ABUNDANTLY

Words and Music by Yohann Anderson

C F
1. **From mountains high, cool waters flow,**
G C
the singing breeze, green meadows grow.
F
Shine tall pine trees, blue sky above,
G C G C
Are all expressions of my Lord's love.
A^m E^m
And this one God who made all these,
F G^7 C G C
Is int'rested in you and me;
A^m E^m
His greatest gift is to make us free,
F G C G C
New self, more life, abundantly.

2. **God speaks, He acts, what He says He will,**
His promises He will fulfill;
Through Christ His focused love appears,
To put at ease the life that fears.
Relationships to all He brings,
The solid feel inside me rings;
No phony do I have to be,
For God, through Christ, accepts just me.

3. **The dawning sun, a bright new light,**
For folks to join, no need to fight;
Creation through variety
Displays God's plan for unity.
And this one God who made all these,
Is interested in you and me;
His greatest gift is to make us free,
New self, more life, abundantly.

IT'S A HAPPY DAY AND I THANK GOD 26

Words and Music by Gary Pfeiffer

(Key of E)

```
                 E E7    A  B   A/C# C#m    E   B
It's a happy day, and I thank God for the weather,
  E            E7           A      F#m     B  C#
It's a happy day, and I'm living it for my Lord;
  B            E E7       A   B     A  C#m E B
It's a happy day, and things are gonna get better:
 F#m           E           F#m    E A  B   E A E
Livin' each day by the promises in God's Word.
```

(Key of D)

```
                 D   D7 G                    A7sus A7
It's a happy day, and I thank God for the weather,
  A              D   D7        G              A7
It's a happy day, and I'm living it for my Lord;
  A             D    D7  G                   A7sus A7
It's a happy day, and things are gonna get better:
  Em           D            G     A         D
Livin' each day by the promises in God's Word.
```

27 THE BUILDING BLOCK

Words and Music by Noel Paul Stookey

Chorus:

```
 A    A7      D                                         A
The building block (building block) that was rejected,
                Esus     E7                         A
became the cornerstone of the whole new world.
 A    A7      D                                        A
The building block (building block) that was rejected,
                Esus     E7                        A
became the cornerstone of the whole new world. (repeat)
```

```
          A7          E E7              D                Esus E7
1.    When I am down and unsuspected with a burden
                          A
      that does not show
        A7               D             A
      I think what time has resurrected
                     B7    C E7                   A
      And how the sun can make the water flow.
```

(Chorus)

2. There is a man who has collected
all the sorrow in our eyes.
He gives us love as God directed
But is seldom recognized.

(Chorus)

3. When all your dreams have been connected
and your vision has been returned
Remember love you are protected
by the truth your heart has learned.

```
          A7        D                                          A
      The building block (building block) that was rejected,
                     Esus7
      became the cornerstone, became the cornerstone,
                                                    D  A
      became the cornerstone of the whole new world.
```

DESPERADO

Words and Music by Don Henley and Glenn Frey

G^7 C C^7 F F^m
1. Desperado, why don't you come to your senses?'
C A^m D^7 G
You've been out ridin' fences for so long now.

C
Oh, you're a hard one,
C^7 F F^m
I know that you've got your reasons
C A^m D^7 G^7
These things that are pleasin' you can hurt you somehow.
C A^m E^m
Don't you draw the queen of diamonds boy,
F C
she'll beat you if she's able
A^m F
you know the queen of hearts is always your best bet.
C A^m E^m
Now it seems to me some fine things
F C
have been laid upon your table
A^m D^7 G
but you only want the ones that you can't get.

2. Desperado, oh you ain't getting no younger
Your pain and your hunger are drivin' you home
And freedom, oh freedom,
well that's just some people talkin'
Your prison is walking through the world all alone.
Don't your feet get cold in the wintertime
Sky won't snow and the sun won't shine
It's hard to tell the night-time from the day
You're losin' all your highs and lows
Ain't it funny how the feelin' goes away.

3. Desperado, why don't you come to your senses,
Come down from your fences and open the gate
It may be rainin', but there's a rainbow above you
C A^m F D^m
You better let somebody love you (let somebody love you)
C A^m D^{m7} C C^7 F F^m C
You better let somebody love you before it's too late.

29

IF

Words and Music by David Gates

1.

F   C
If a picture paints a thousand words,
Cm   B♭6(9)
then why can't I paint you?
B♭m6(9)   F
The words will never show
B♭m6   C7
the you I've come to know.
F   C
If a face could launch a thousand ships,
Cm   B♭m6(9)
then where am I to go?
B♭m6(9)   F
There's no one home but you;
B♭m6   C7
you're all that's left me, too.
C7sus Dm   D♭   F   B♭6
And when my love for life is running dry,
Am7-5   D7   Gm7   C7
You come and pour yourself on me.

2.

If a man could be two places
at one time I'd be with you
Tomorrow and today, beside you all the way.
If the world should stop revolving,
spinning slowly down to die,
I'd spend the end with you
and when the world was through,
C7sus Dm   D♭   F   B♭6
Then one by one the stars would all go out,
Am7-5   D7   Gm7 C7sus C7 F Gm7 B m6 F
Then you and I would simply fly away.

30 FATHER AND SON

Words and Music by Cat Stevens

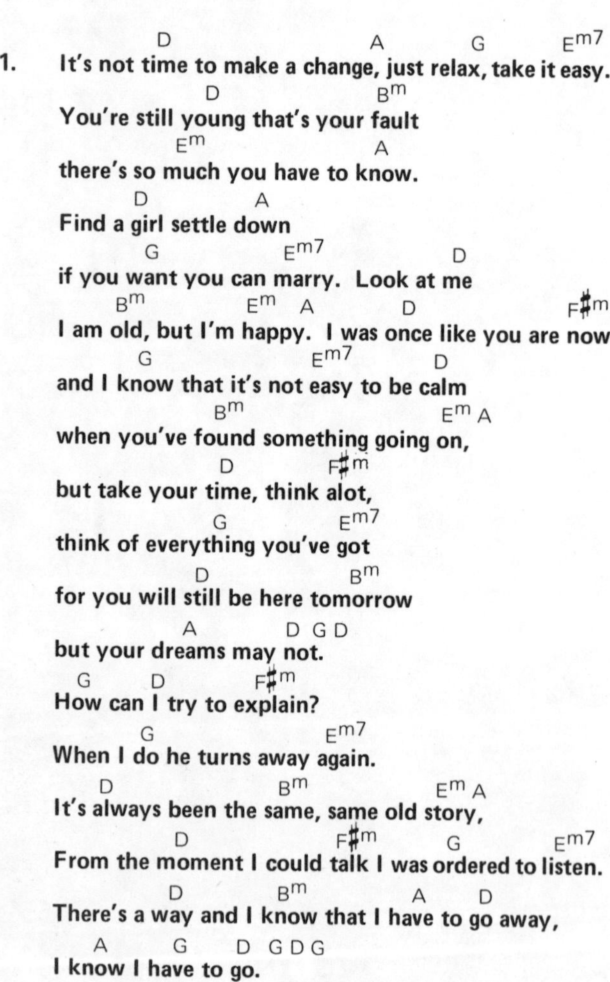

```
             D                      A          G          Em7
1.    It's not time to make a change, just relax, take it easy.
                 D              Bm
      You're still young that's your fault
                Em                  A
      there's so much you have to know.
           D         A
      Find a girl settle down
           G           Em7          D
      if you want you can marry.  Look at me
          Bm       Em   A      D                   F#m
      I am old, but I'm happy.  I was once like you are now
            G            Em7       D
      and I know that it's not easy to be calm
                     Bm              Em A
      when you've found something going on,
                     D         F#m
      but take your time, think alot,
                     G        Em7
      think of everything you've got
                   D          Bm
      for you will still be here tomorrow
                  A      D G D
      but your dreams may not.
        G     D       F#m
      How can I try to explain?
             G              Em7
      When I do he turns away again.
           D            Bm            Em A
      It's always been the same, same old story,
                  D            F#m       G          Em7
      From the moment I could talk I was ordered to listen.
                  D        Bm            A     D
      There's a way and I know that I have to go away,
           A      G     D GDG
      I know I have to go.
```

2. It's not time to make a change,
just sit down take it slowly.
You're still young that' your fault.
There's so much you have to go through.
Find a girl settle down
if you want you can marry. Look at me
I am old, but I'm happy. All the times that I've cried
keepin' all the things I knew inside
it's hard but it's harder to ignore it.
If they were right I'd agree

G Em7
but it's them they know — not me.

D Bm A D
Now there's a way and I know that I have to go away,

A G D
I know I have to go.

31 BLESSED ASSURANCE

Words by Fanny J. Crosby
Music by Pheobe Palmer Knapp

Chorus:

```
                    G             D
This is my story, this is my song:
               G          A           A7
Praising my Saviour all the day long.
               D    G          D
This is my story, this is my song:
                 G        A          D
Praising my Saviour all the day long.
```

```
             D                       G        D
1.    Blessed assurance, Jesus is mine!
                            A       E         A
      Oh, what a foretaste of glory divine!
                      D            G              D
      Heir of salvation, purchase of God,
                         G            A                D
      Born of His Spirit, washed in His blood.
```

(Chorus)

2. Perfect submission, perfect delight,
Visions of rapture now burst on my sight.
Angels descending, bring from above
Echoes of mercy, whispers of love.

(Chorus)

3. Perfect submission, all is at rest;
I in my Saviour am happy and blest,
Watching and waiting, looking above,
Filled with His goodness, lost in His love.

(Chorus)

NEW LIFE 32

By Sally Anderson

E♭ Fm B♭sus B♭ Gm/E B♭/G A♭
Behold, I do a new thing among you;
Cm/A6 B♭/G A♭/F B♭sus B♭
Even now I will begin it.
Fm Csus C C7 Fm
But cling not to things that I've already done,
A♭/B♭ B♭7 Gm/E♭ A♭ B♭sus
and let me start a-pressin' you
A♭sus A♭ B♭ B♭7 E♭
For you have much to learn of my glory.
A♭sus A♭ B♭ B♭sus B♭7 E♭
There is so much more I will do!
A♭sus A♭ B♭
So open your hearts, children,
Cm A♭
let my hand create in you
Cm7/B♭ A♭/B B♭7 E♭
The living life of Jesus that redeems your world.

(Chorus)
E♭ F9 Fm9 Fm7 B♭7
Father, I believe you;
Fm/E♭ Gm/E A♭/F Cm/A B♭m/G Cm7/F
Jesus, I receive you;
Fm9/B♭A♭/B♭ E♭ G A♭sus A♭ A♭/F
Holy Spirit, I now free you to create
B♭7 E♭
in me new life.

33 TEACH ME LORD TO WAIT

Words and Music by Stuart Hamblen

C^7 F
They that wait upon the Lord shall renew their strength;
C^7/G F C^7 F
They shall mount up with wings like eagles;
F^7 B♭
They shall run, and not be weary;
F
They shall walk, and not faint.
C^7/G F B♭ F/C C^7 F
Teach me, Lord, teach me, Lord, to wait.

THERE IS A PLACE OF QUIET REST 34

By Cleland B. McAfee, 1901

(Capo 1)

Chorus:
C^7 F C G^7 C
O Jesus, blest Redeemer Sent from the heart of God,
C^7 F C D^m C G^7 C
Hold us who wait before Thee Near to the heart of God.

C G^7
1. There is a place of quiet rest
G G^7 C
Near to the heart of God,
C G^7
A place where sin cannot molest,
G^7 G C G^7 C
Near to the heart of God.

(Chorus)

2. There is a place of comfort sweet
Near to the heart of God,
A place where we our Savior meet,
Near to the heart of God.

(Chorus)

3. There is a place of full release
Near to the heart of God,
A place where all is joy and peace,
Near to the heart of God.

(Chorus)

35 ONE TIN SOLDIER

Words and Music by Dennis Lambert and Brian Potter

(Key of C – good group key)

Chorus:

D   F♯m
Go ahead and hate your neighbor,
G   D
Go ahead and cheat a friend.
                                F♯m   G   D
Do it in the name of heaven you can justify it in the end.
                                                F♯m
There won't be any trumpets blowin'
   G   D   G
Come the judgment day on the bloody morning after
                                 D G D G D
One Tin Soldier rides away.

D A Bm Bm/A
1. Listen children to a story that was written long ago
G D
'Bout a kingdom on a mountain
Em7 Em7
and the valley folk below.
D A
On the mountain was a treasure
Bm Bm/A
buried deep beneath a stone
G D
And the valley people swore
Em7 Em7/A D
they'd have it for their very own.

2. So the people of the valley sent a message up the hill
asking for the buried treasure
tons of gold for which they'd kill.
Came an answer from the kingdom
"With our brothers we will share
all the secrets of our mountain,
all the riches buried there."

3. Now the valley cried with anger
mount your horses, draw your sword
and they killed the mountain people
so they won their just reward.
Now they stood beside the treasure
on the mountain, dark and red
turned the stone and looked beneath it
"Peace on earth" was all it said.

36 JOHN HENRY BOSWORTH

Words and Music by Noel Stookey

Chorus:

G C/G G^{7} C/G
With a song that he'd been singing,
G C/G G^{7} C/G
and they waved to the people that they passed,
G C/G G^{7} C/G
all along the highway they went winging
G D^{7} C/G
headed for their paradise at last.

AG A^{sus} A
1. **John Henry Bosworth, late in sixty eight,**
C C^{2} C G
decided that the time had come to settle his estate.
A^{sus} A
The riots of the summer were creeping into fall,
C C^{2}
So he packed his family in the car
C G
and chose to leave it all.
B^{m} add G A^{m} G
Out on the open road with his elbow in the breeze,

he pulled his woman to him
D^{7} G
and he gave her heart a squeeze.

(Chorus)

2. John Henry Bosworth's family on the farm,
Elizabeth is sitting, knitting from a ball of yarn.
Koolaid's in the kitchen, Button's up in her bed,
And John he takes a long pull on
his pipe and lays his head
back in the easy chair, with the Good Book in his hand
he closed his eyes and thanked the Lord
for making him a lucky man.

(Chorus)

3. John Henry Bosworth, nineteen eighty four,
The city's dead, the sky is red
and there's a knock upon the door.
Ev'ry piece of Scripture and ev'ry prayer he prayed
had brought him this moment of this particular day.
"Open the doors," he cried
"Let the brothers and sisters inside,
I've got everything to give now
and nothing left to hide."

(Chorus) then:

C/G G^7 C/G
And I was wondering if you had been to the mountain
C/G G
to look at the valley below?
C/G G^7 C/G
Did you see all the roads tangled down in the valley,
C/G G
Did you know which way to go?
C A^m C/G D^7 G
Mm, the mountain stream runs pure and clear
C A^{m7} C/G D^7 G
and I wish to my soul I could always be here.
C/G G^7 C
But there's a reason for living way down in the valley
G D^7 C G C G
that only the mountain knows.

37 LORD'S PRAYER

Words and Music by John Fischer

Cmj7 Dm7 Cmj7 Dm7
1. Holy Father hear our prayer,
Cmj7 Dm7 Em7 Dm7
Keep us always in your care;
Fmj7 Em7 Fmj7 G
May your kingdom come to us,
Cmj7 Dm7 Em7 Dm7 Cmj7
And may we learn how to trust.

2. Do your will among us now,
As we here before you bow.
Give to us but what we need,
As upon your word we feed.

3. Forgive us for the things that we have not done,
When we've failed before we've yet begun;
And may we as children of Yours
Give forgiveness in return.

4. Keep us from the things that do you wrong,
When we're weak because we think we're strong.
Save us from our selfish desire;
Fill us with your love inspire.

5. Honor, greatness belong to you,
Love and peace and mercy, too!
Praise to you again and again!
Amen.

BE STILL, MY SOUL 38

Traditional

Words by Katharina von Schlegel
Music by Jean Sibelius

```
   F   C7  F   C7   F   C7  F Bb C7  C F
1. Be still, my soul; the Lord is on thy side.
    F  C7  F C7  F  C7   F  Bb C7   F
   Bear patiently the cross of grief or pain;
                  Dm        F        C Gm
   Leave to thy God to order and provide.
          D Gm F      Bb             A
   In ev'ry change He faithful will remain.
   F              Dm             F        C    Gm
   Be still, my soul; thy best, thy heav'nly Friend
   Gm    D  Gm   F                C7      F
   Thro' thorny ways leads to a joyful end.
```

2. Be still, my soul; thy God doth undertake
To guide the future as He has the past.
Thy hope, thy confidence let nothing shake;
All now mysterious shall be bright at last.
Be still, my soul; the waves and winds still know
His voice who ruled them while He dwelt below.

3. Be still, my soul; the hour is hast'ning on
When we shall be forever with the Lord,
When disappointment, grief, and fear are gone,
Sorrow forgot, love's purest joys restored.
Be still, my soul; when change and tears are past,
All safe and blessed we shall meet at last.

39 WERE YOU THERE

Traditional Spiritual

(Guitar Key C)

Slowly

Chorus:

```
C F C
Oh!
  F       C          Am                   F          F           F   G7
Sometimes it causes me to tremble, tremble, tremble,
  C       F      C                      F    G7               C
Were you there when they crucified my Lord?
  F              C
(Were you there?)
```

```
            C                                       G7               C
1.     Were you there when they crucified my Lord?
            F                C
       (Were you there?)
            C               Em                           F    C              G7
       Were you there when they crucified my Lord?
            F                G7
       (Were you there?)
```

(Chorus)

2. Were you there when they nailed Him to the tree?
(Were you there?)
Were you there when they nailed Him to the tree?
(Were you there?)

(Chorus)

3. Were you there when they pierced Him in the side?
(Were you there?)
Were you there when they pierced Him in the side?
(Were you there?)

(Chorus)

4. Were you there when they laid Him in the tomb?
(Were you there?)
Were you there when they laid Him in the tomb?
(Were you there?)

(Chorus)

5. Were you there when He rose up from the dead?
(Were you there?)
Were you there when He rose up from the dead?
(Were you there?)
Oh!
Sometimes I feel like shouting glory, glory, glory!
Were you there when He rose up from the dead?
(Were you there?)

40 WHEN THE SAINTS GO MARCHING IN

New Words and Music added by Bill Hansen (ASCAP)

```
     G7      C             F
1.   We are walking in the footsteps
          C              Am        Dm7 G7
     of those who've walked before,
              C        F
     and we'll all be reunited
             C          Dm7 G7  C
     on that great far distant shore.
                       C
     Oh, when the saints go marching in,
                       C              G7
     Oh, when the saints go marching in,
              C Cmaj7 C7           F  Fm7
     Oh, I want to be in that number,
                C    Am    Dm7 G7 C
     When the saints go marching in.
```

2. **Oh, our hearts will swell with gladness**
When we join that mighty throng
And there'll be no sign of sadness
When old Gabriel blows his horn.

Oh, when we hear old Gabriel blow,
Oh, when we hear old Gabriel blow
We will all be in that number
When we hear old Gabriel blow.

3. **There's green pastures waiting for us**
There'll be pie high in the sky
There's a great day coming for us
When the saints go marching by.

Oh, when the Judgment day is here
Oh, when the Judgment day is here
Oh, I want to be in that number
When the Judgment day is here.

```
  C    E   Dm7 G7 C
(Judgment Day is here.)
```

I WILL SING 41

Psalm 104:33, 34, 35
By Donya Brockway

D D A G D
I will sing unto the Lord as long as I live.
Em A D Em7 F♯m A/E
I will sing praise to my God while I have my being.
D D A G D
My meditation of Him shall be sweet.
Em7 A7 D Em7 D
I will be glad, I will be glad in the Lord.
D7 G A
Bless thou the Lord, Oh my soul,
D A♭ Bm D/A G
Praise ye the Lord. Bless thou the Lord,
A D G/D D7
Oh my soul, Praise ye the Lord.
G A
Bless thou the Lord, Oh my soul,
D A6 Bm D/A G
Praise ye the Lord. Bless thou the Lord,
A A7 D G/D D
Oh my soul, Praise ye the Lord.

42 AMEN

Traditional

Starts with chorus of Amen
Amen
Amen, Amen, Amen.

E E
Solo: **See the baby . . . . lyin' in a manger**
Chorus: **. . . . . Amen . . . .**

Solo: **. . . . On Christmas morning**
Chorus: **Amen . . . .**
E A E A E B^7 E
Chorus: **Amen. Amen. Amen.**

2. See Him at the Temple
Talkin' to the elders
Who marvelled at His wisdom.

3. First He came a preachin'
Then He came a teachin'
Tellin' them disciples

4. See Him in the garden
Talkin' to the Father
In deepest sorrow

5. Went before Pilate
Then they crucified Him
But He rose on Easter

43 VICTORIOUS WARRIOR

By Marj Snyder

C B^{m7} A^{m7} G
oo — oo — oo —

C B^{m7}
The Lord your God is in your midst a victorious warrior.
A^{m7} G
He will exalt over you with joy.

          C   Bm7
He will be quiet in His love.

Am7   G   G
He will rejoice over you with shouts of joy.

C   Bm7
Shout for joy oh Daughter of Zion.

Am7   G
Shout in triumph, oh Israel.

C   Bm7
Rejoice and exalt with all your heart,

Am7   G
Oh daughter of Jerusalem.

                  C   Bm7
The Lord has taken away His judgments against you.

Am7   G
He has cleared away your enemies.

                  C   Bm7
The King of Israel, the Lord, is in your midst.

Am7   G
You will fear disaster no more.

C   Bm7
In that day it will be said to Jerusalem

Am7   G
Do not be afraid, oh Zion.

C   Bm7
Do not let your hands fall limp,

     Am7   G
the Lord your God He is in your midst.

G   C   Bm7
The Lord your God is in your midst a victorious warrior.

Bm7   G   C   Bm7
He will exalt over you with joy. He will be quiet in His love.

Am7   G   G
He will rejoice over you with shouts of joy.

C   Bm7 Am7 G
oo — oo — oo —

44 LET US BREAK BREAD TOGETHER

Traditional Spiritual

(Capo 1)
Guitar—Key of D

Chorus:

```
  D     B   A        D7
When I fall on my knees,
              Em               G    A7
With my face to the rising sun,
     D      Bm    G      A7  D G D
O Lord, have mercy on me.
```

```
         A7        D       G        D      Em A7   D G
1.    Let us break bread together on our knees;
       D  A7  D     A       D         E7       A A7
      Let us break bread together on our knees.
```

2. Let us drink the cup together on our knees;
   Let us drink the cup together on our knees.

3. Let us praise God together on our knees;
   Let us praise God together on our knees.

45 • YOU'VE GOT A FRIEND

Words and Music by Carole King

```
                      Am            E7
1.    When you're down and troubled
                  Am          E7          Am E7 Am
      and you need some love and care,
           Dm7         G          G7     C Dm C
      and nothin', nothin' is going' right,
      Bm7                         E7
      Close your eyes and think of me
          Am   E7           Am E7
      and soon I will be there
          Dm7          Em7                 F6 G F6
      to brighten up even your darkest night.
```

```
         C
You just call out my name
          F
and you know wherever I am
             C                  F/G
I'll come runnin' to see you again.
  C                      Cmaj7
Winter, spring, summer or fall,
F                      C6 C7
All you have to do is call
           F Em7 Dm7 F6            C F F C Dm C Bm7 Em7
and I'll be there — You've got a friend.

2.  If the sky above you grows dark and full of clouds
and that ol' north wind begins to blow,
Keep your head together and call my name out loud.
Soon you'll hear me knockin' at your door.
You just call out my name
and you know wherever I am
I'll come runnin' to see you again.
Winter, spring, summer and fall,
F                       C6 C7            F              Em7 Dm7 F6
all you have to do is call and I'll be there, Yes I will —
     B                              F
Now ain't it good to know that you've got a friend
       C                  Cmaj7
When people can be so cold?
          F                Bb7
They'll hurt you, yes, and desert you
     Am                   D7
and take your soul if you let them.
          Dm7
Oh, but don't you let them.

You just call out my name
and you know wherever I am
I'll come runnin' to see you again.
Winter, spring, summer or fall,
all you have to do is call and I'll be there, Yes I will
You've got a friend.
```

46 THERE IS A BALM IN GILEAD

Traditional Spiritual

Chorus:

```
 D7        G  D7   G
There is a balm in Gilead
                  C         D7
To make the wounded whole,
 D7        G  D7   G
There is a balm in Gilead
 C  G        D7      G
To heal the sinsick soul.
```

```
           G               D7  G
1.    Sometimes I feel discouraged,
        D7  G                 D7
      And think my work's in vain,
       G                   D7  G7
      But then the Holy Spirit
       C   G          D7 G  C
      Revives my soul again.
```

(Chorus)

2. If you cannot preach like Peter,
If you cannot pray like Paul,
You can tell the love of Jesus,
And say, "He died for all."

(Chorus)

47 WEDDING SONG

Words and Music by Noel Paul Stookey

Noel plays this song on "Sebastian," a specially built twelve-string guitar. It is tuned a minor third below concert pitch so that this song is played out of "G" position although it sounds in E major. Either tune down or capo up as desired.

```
       G                                  D
He is now to be among you at the calling of your hearts,
C                                                G
Rest assured this troubador is acting on His part.
```

G D C G
The union of your spirits here has caused Him to remain,
Em G D
for whenever two or more of you are gathered in His name
C G A Cmaj7 G
there is love, there is love.
G D
Well, a man shall leave his mother
C G
and a woman leave her home,
Em G D
they shall travel on to where the two shall be as one.
G D C G
As it was in the beginning, is now, and 'til the end,
Em G D
woman draws her life from man and gives it back again,
C G A Cmaj7 G
and there is love, there is love.
C Am7
Well then, what's to be the reason
D G
for becoming man and wife?
C Am7 D G
Is it love that brings you here, or love that brings you life?
G D C G
For if loving is the answer, then who's the giving for?
Em G D
Do you believe in something that you've never seen before?
C G A Cmaj7 G G D Em G D
Oh, there's love, oh, there's love.
G D
Oh, the marriage of your spirits
C G
here has caused Him to remain,
Em G D
for whenever two or more of you are gathered in His name,
C G A Cmaj7 G
there is love, Oh, there's love.

48 JOYFUL, JOYFUL, WE ADORE THEE

Words by Henry Van Dyke   Arr. from Ludwig Van Beethoven

G D^7 G^7 D^7 G D^7
1. Joyful, joyful, we adore Thee,
G D G D
God of glory, Lord of love;
G G^7 C G A^m
Hearts unfold like flow'rs before Thee,
G D G D^7 G
Opening to the sun above.
D G D^7 G
Melt the clouds of sin and sadness;
D^7 B E^m A D
Drive the dark of doubt away;
G G^7 C A^m
Giver of immortal gladness,
G D G D^7 G
Fill us with the light of day!

2. All Thy works with joy surround Thee;
Earth and heav'n reflect Thy rays;
Stars and angels sing around Thee,
Center of unbroken praise.
Field and forest, vale and mountain,
Flowery meadow, flashing sea,
Chanting bird and flowing fountain
Call us to rejoice in Thee.

3. Thou art giving and forgiving,
Ever blessing, ever blest,
Wellspring of the joy of living,
Ocean depth of happy rest!
Thou our Father, Christ our Brother –
All who live in love are Thine.
Teach us how to love each other;
Lift us to the joy divine.

4. Mortals join the mighty chorus
Which the morning stars began.
Fatherlove is reigning o'er us;
Brotherlove binds man to man.
Ever singing, march we onward,
Victors in the midst of strife;
Joyful music leads us sunward
In the triumph song of life.

HAMMER SONG

Words and Music by Lee Hays and Pete Seeger

C C F G C
1. **If I had a hammer, I'd hammer in the mornin,'**
G C Em F G G7
I'd hammer in the evenin', all over this land;
C Am
I'd hammer out danger, I'd hammer out warnin,'
F C
I'd hammer out love between
F C
my brothers and my sisters,
F C G C Em F G7
all — all over this land.
C Em F
Oo oo oo —

2. **If I had a bell, I'd ring it in the mornin'.**
I'd ring it in the evenin' all over this land;
I'd ring out danger, I'd ring out warning,
I'd ring out love between my brothers and my sisters,
All — all over this land.
Oo oo oo —

3. **If I had a song, I'd sing it in the mornin'.**
I'd sing it in the evenin' all over this land;
I'd sing out danger, I'd sing out warning,
I'd sing out love between my brothers and my sisters,
All — all over this land.
Oo oo oo —

4. **Well I got a hammer and I got a bell**
And I got a song to sing all over this land;
It's the hammer of justice, It's the bell of freedom,
It's the song about love between
my brothers and my sisters,
All — all over this land.

50 JESUS IS THE ANSWER

Words and Music by Andrae Crouch and Sandra Crouch

Chorus:

F   Am7   Dm   F7
Jesus is the answer for the world today,
  B♭   F   Gm7   C
Above Him there's no other, Jesus is the way.
F   Am7 Dm   F7
Jesus is the answer for the world today,
  B♭   F   Gm7 B♭   F
Above Him there's no other, Jesus is the way.

F   Am7   Dm   F7
1. **If you have some questions in the corners of your mind,**
  B♭   F   Gm7   C
Traces of discouragement and peace you cannot find.
   F   Am   Dm   F7
Reflections of your past seem to face you ev'ry day,
     B   F   Gm7 B♭maj7 F
But this one thing I do know: Jesus is the way.

(Chorus)

2. **I know you've got mountains**
that you think you cannot climb,
I know your skies are dark,
you think the sun won't shine.
In case you don't know, but the Word of God is true,
And ev'rything He's promised, He will do it for you.

(Chorus)

HE AIN'T HEAVY . . . HE'S MY BROTHER 51

Words by Bob Russell
Music by Bobby Scott

Bm7 A E D Bm7
1. The road is long — with many a winding turn,
E7 F♯m G Bm7
that leads us to who knows where, who knows where.
Amaj7 E Dmaj9
But I'm strong, strong enough to carry him;
Bm7 A
He ain't heavy . . . He's my brother.

2. So on we go; his welfare is my concern.
No burden is he to bear, we'll get there.
For I know he would not encumber me;
He ain't heavy . . . He's my brother.

A Dmaj7 E Dmaj7 E
If I'm laden at all, I'm laden with sadness
C♯m Em7 Dmaj7
that ev'ryone's heart isn't filled
F♯m Dm7 F♯m Bm7 E7
with the gladness of love for one another.
Bm7 A E D Bm7
It's a long, long road, from which there is no return.
E F♯m G Bm7
While we're on our way to there, why not share?
Amaj7 E Dmaj9
And the load doesn't weigh me down at all;
Bm7 E7 A Bm7 A
He ain't heavy . . . He's my brother.

FAREWELL ANDROMEDA

Words and Music by John Denver

```
     F                           Gm7           Csus4
1.   Welcome to my mornin', welcome to my day,
              F
     oh, yes, I'm the one responsible,
       Gm7              Csus4           F
     I made it just this way to make myself some pictures,
     Gm7                 Csus4
     see what they might bring.
        F                           Gm7                  Csus4
     I think I made it perfectly, I wouldn't change a thing.
        F     Gm7  Csus4     F    Gm7  Csus4
     La la la la la la la la, la la la la la la la la.
```

2. Welcome to my happiness,
you know it makes me smile,
and it pleases me to have you here
for just a little while,
while we open up the spaces
and try to break some chains.
And if the truth is told they will never come again.
La la la la la la la la, la la la la la la.

Welcome to my evenin' the closin' of the day,
you know I could try a million times,
never find a better way to tell you that I love you
and all the songs I played are to thank you
for allowing me in the lovely day you made.

(Repeat first verse)

A MIGHTY FORTRESS IS OUR GOD 53

Words and Music by Martin Luther
Trans. by Frederick H. Hedge

C Em G Am D7
1. A mighty fortress is our God,
Am Em F C F Dm G7 C
A bulwark never failing;
C G Am D7 G
Our helper He, amid the flood
Am Em F C F Dm7 G7 C
Of mortal ills prevailing:
Em Am D4 D7 G C F E7/G Am
For still our ancient foe Doth seek to work us woe;
E7 Am E F C
His craft and power are great,
F F Dm E
And, armed with cruel hate,
Am Em F C F Dm G7 C
On earth is not his equal.

2. Did we in our own strength confide,
Our striving would be losing;
Were not the right Man on our side,
The Man of God's own choosing:
Dost ask who that may be? Christ Jesus, it is He,
Lord Sabaoth, His name, From age to age the same,
And He must win the battle.

3. And though this world, with devils filled,
Should threaten to undo us,
We will not fear, for God hath willed
His truth to triumph through us:
The Prince of Darkness grim — We tremble not for him;
His rage we can endure, For lo, his doom is sure,
One little word shall fell him.

4. That word above all earthly powers,
No thanks to them, abideth;
The Spirit and the gifts are ours
Thro' Him who with us sideth:
Let goods and kindred go, This mortal life also;
The body they may kill: God's truth abideth still,
His kingdom is forever.

54 WHEN I SURVEY THE WONDROUS CROSS

Words by Isaac Watts
Music by Lowell Mason
Based on Psalm Tone I

F C F C B♭ C F
1. **When I survey the wondrous cross**
B♭ F B♭ C
On which the Prince of glory died,
F C F B♭ C F
My richest gain I count but loss,
C Dm B♭ C F
And pour contempt on all my pride.

2. **Forbid it, Lord, that I should boast,**
Save in the death of Christ my God;
All the vain things that charm me most,
I sacrifice them to His blood.

3. **See, from His head, His hands, His feet,**
Sorrow and love flow mingled down –
Did e'er such love and sorrow meet,
Or thorns compose so rich a crown?

4. **Were the whole realm of nature mine,**
That were a present far too small;
Love so amazing, so divine,
Demands my soul, my life, my all.

I SHALL BE RELEASED

Words and Music by Bob Dylan

Chorus:

A Bm
I see my light come shining
C#m Bm A E7
From the west unto the east.
A Bm
Any day now, any day now,
C#m Bm A
I shall be released.

1\. A Bm
They say ev'rything can be replaced,
C#m Bm A E7
Yet ev'ry distance is not near.
A Bm
So I remember ev'ry face
C#m Bm A E7
Of ev'ry man who put me here.

(Chorus)

2\. They say ev'ry man needs protection,
They say ev'ry man must fall.
Yet I swear I see my reflection
Some place so high above this wall.

(Chorus)

A Bm
Standing next to me in this lonely crowd,
C m Bm A E7
Is a man who swears he's not to blame.
A B
All day long I hear him shout so loud,
C m Bm A
Crying out that he was framed.

(Chorus)

56 GLORY TO THE LAMB

Words and Music by Rick Motter and Greg Lanson

C F C F C
Chorus: Glory to the Lamb – Glory to the Lamb –
Am G F C G G7
Glory to the Lamb of God.

C G
1. Lord, I've just come today,
F Fmin
to ask you to guide my way,
C G
I know there's trials that I must face,
F Fmin
but I'll overcome by your grace.
Am F
That people would see Jesus in me,
C G
He's the hope of glory.

2. Prince of Peace, King of Kings,
Almighty God is He.
Tree of life, living bread.
Many hungry souls He's fed.
If you would only turn to Him,
Come to the Lord, forsake your sin.
Am F
Jesus would come and set you free –
C G G7
Make you how you ought to be.

57 FIRE AND RAIN

Words and Music by James Taylor

Chorus:
F F/E Dm7 G7 C
I've seen fire and I seen rain
F F/E Dm7 G7 C
I've seen sunny days that I thought would never end

F F/E Dm7 G7 C
I've seen lonely times when I could not find a friend
B♭ F/A Gm7 C9
But I always thought that I'd see you again.

C Gm7
1. Just yesterday morning
F C
they let me know you were gone
C G B♭ maj7
Susan, the plans they made put an end to you
C Gm7 F C
I walked out this morning and I wrote down this song
C G B♭ maj7
I just can't remember who to send it to.

(Chorus)

2. Look down upon me, Jesus,
you've got to make a stand
You've just got to see me through another day
My body's aching and my time is at hand
And I won't make it any other way.

(Chorus)

C Gm7/C
3. Walking my mind to an easy time,
F/C C
my back towards the sun
G
Lord knows, when the cold wind blows
B♭/C
it'll turn your head around
C Gm7/C
Well, there's hours of time on the telephone line
F/C C
to talk about things to come
C G
Sweet dreams and flying machines
B♭/C
in pieces on the ground.

(Chorus)

58 TRUST AND OBEY

Words by John H. Sammis
Music by Daniel B. Towner

Chorus:

C F D G^m
Trust and obey, for there's no other way
C^7 F B♭ F C F
To be happy in Jesus, But to trust and obey.

(C^7) F C F
1. When we walk with the Lord
C F
In the light of His word,
B♭ F C
What a glory He sheds on our way!
F C F
While we do His good will,
C F
He abides with us still
B♭ F C F
And with all who will trust and obey.

2. Not a shadow can rise,
Not a cloud in the skies,
But His smile quickly drives it away;
Not a doubt nor a fear,
Not a sigh nor a tear
Can abide while we trust and obey.

3. But we never can prove
The delights of His love
Until all on the altar we lay;
For the favor He shows
And the joy He bestows
Are for them who will trust and obey.

4. Then in fellowship sweet
We will sit at His feet,
Or we'll walk by His side in the way;
What He says we will do,
Where He sends we will go —
Never fear, only trust and obey.

younglife

59 SWEET BABY JAMES

Words and Music by James Taylor

Chorus:

```
   D                  G              Em7/A D
Goodnight, you moonlight ladies,
 Bm            G           D
Rockabye, sweet Baby James.
 Bm                  G             D
Deep greens and blues are the colors I choose,
            Bm7            E7           Asus4
Won't you let me go down in my dreams,
A7    G            A7           D
And rockabye, sweet Baby James.
```

```
        D              A7              G              F#m
1.  There is a young cowboy, he lives on the range.
        Bm                F#m Bm        D          F#m
    His horse and his cattle are his only companions;
        Bm          F#m                 D                F#m
    He works in the saddle and he sleeps in the canyons
      G          D                   A7           Em7 A7
    Waiting for summer his pastures to change.
        G                             Em7/A       D
    And as the moon rises he sits by his fire —
       Bm               G                  D         A7
    Thinking 'bout women and glasses of beer
         G                              Em7/A   D
    And closing his eyes as the doggies retire,
        Bm           G                D
    He sings out a song which is soft but it's clear
       Bm7          E7            A7sus4 A7
    As if maybe someone could hear.
```

(Chorus)

2. Now the first of December was covered with snow
So was the turnpike from Stockbridge to Boston.
The Berkshires seemed dreamlike
on account of that frosting,
With ten miles behind me and ten thousand more to go.
There's a song that they sing
when they take to the highway
A song that they sing when they take to the sea,
A song that they sing of their home in the sky,
Maybe you can believe it if it helps you to sleep,
But singing works just fine for me.

(Chorus)

SUNNY SKIES

Words and Music by James Taylor

Cmaj7 Dm7 G11
1. Sunny skies sleeps in the morning
Cmaj7 Dm7 G11
He doesn't know when to rise
Cmaj7 Dm7 G7 Cmaj7
He closes his weary eyes upon the day
Dm7 G11 Cmaj7
Look at him yawning
Dm7 G11 Cmaj7
Throwing his mornin' hours away
Dm7 C9 Cmaj7
He knows how to ease down slow.
Dm7 G11 C
Ev'rything is fine in the end
Dm7 G9 Cmaj7
And you will be pleased to know
Dm7/G
That sunny skies hasn't a friend.

2. Sunny skies weeps in the evening
It doesn't much matter why
I guess he just has to cry from time to time
Ev'ryone's leaving
And sunny skies has to stay behind
He knows how to ease down slow.
Ev'rything is fine in the end
And you will be pleased to know
That sunny skies hasn't a friend.

Cmaj7 Dm7 G11

3. **Sunny skies sleeps in the morning**

Cmaj7 Dm7 G11

He doesn't know when to rise

Cmaj7 Dm7 G7 Cmaj7

He closes his weary eyes upon the day

Dm7 G11 Cmaj7 F6/G Cmaj7 F6/G

And throws it all away.

G9 Cmaj7

Looking at the snow and trees

F6/G Cmaj7 F6/G

that grow outside my window

G9 Cmaj7 F6/G Cmaj7 F6/G

Looking at the things that pass me by

G9 Cmaj7 F6/G Cmaj7

Wondering if where I've been is worth the things

F6/G Cmaj7 F6/G

I've been through

G7 Cmaj7

Ending with a friend named sunny skies.

61 DOESN'T THAT BIBLE SAY (WE SHALL OVERCOME)

Words and Music by Greg Lanson

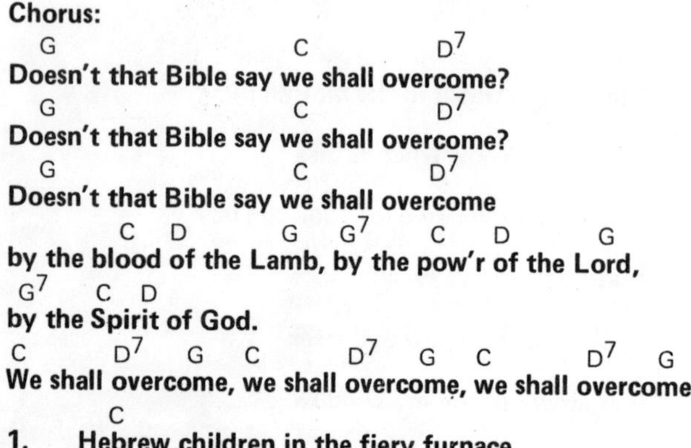

Chorus:

```
  G                         C            D7
Doesn't that Bible say we shall overcome?
  G                         C            D7
Doesn't that Bible say we shall overcome?
  G                         C           D7
Doesn't that Bible say we shall overcome
          C   D          G   G7     C     D        G
by the blood of the Lamb, by the pow'r of the Lord,
 G7     C  D
by the Spirit of God.
C         D7     G   C           D7    G   C           D7    G
We shall overcome, we shall overcome, we shall overcome.
```

```
            C
1.     Hebrew children in the fiery furnace,
         D
       Daniel in the Lion's den,
         C
       What did they do when things got tough?
             D7
       They put their trust in Him — Oh,
```

(Chorus)

2. Jonah was down in the belly of a whale,
Elijah was challenging the prophets of Baal,
Noah's in the ark with out a sail,
They knew that God would never fail.

(Chorus)

3. Joseph was in Egypt all alone,
David slew Goliath with a sling and stone,
Samson killed an army with a donkey's bone,
Their faith in God the world was shown.

(Chorus)

PASS IT ON

62

Words and Music by Kurt Kaiser

```
      D            F#m       G         A
1.    It only takes a spark to get a fire going
          D              F#m
      And soon all those around
          G               A
      Can warm up to its glowing.
        D     G              D
      That's how it is with God's love
       Em     A     Dmaj7       Bm
      Once you've experienced it;
           Em7                  D
      You spread His love to ev'ryone;
           G       A      D
      You want to PASS IT ON.
```

2. What a wondrous time is spring
when all the trees are budding
The birds begin to sing,
The flowers start their blooming
That's how it is with God's love
Once you've experienced it;
You want to sing It's fresh like spring
You want to PASS IT ON.

3. I wish for you my friend
this happiness that I've found.
You can depend on Him,
it matters not where you're bound
I'll shout it from the mountain top
I want my world to know;
The Lord of love has come to me,
I want to PASS IT ON.

```
          G                   D
      I'll shout it from the mountain top,
      Em  A     Dmaj7       Bm
      I want my world to know,
           Em7                 D
      The Lord of love has come to me,
          G       A      D
      I want to PASS IT ON.
```

63 LONELY PEOPLE

Words and Music by Daniel Peek

C Am Em
1. This is for all the lonely people
C Am Em G
thinking that life has passed them by.
F G C Am7 C
Don't give up until you drink from the silver cup
F G C G
and ride that highway in the sky.

2. This is for all the single people
thinking that love has left them dry.
Don't give up until you drink from the silver cup,
you never know until you try.

F F/E Dm7 F F/E Dm7
Well, I'm on my way, yes, I'm back to stay,
F F/E Dm7 G C G
Well, I'm on my way back home.
C Am Em
This is for all the lonely people
C Am Em G
thinking that life has passed them by.
F G C Am7 C
Don't give up until you drink from the silver cup
F G C Am7 C/G
and never take you down or never give you up,
F G Am
you never know until you try.

FILL MY CUP 64

Traditional

E
Fill my cup, let it overflow.
E B^7
Fill my cup, let it overflow.
E A E B^7 E
Fill my cup, let it overflow, let it overflow with love.

65 SEEK AND YE SHALL FIND

Traditional

C
Chorus: Seek and you shall find.
F
Knock and the door shall be opened.
A^m
Ask and it shall be given.
F G C
And a love come a tum-ba-lin' down.

C
1. On ev'ry door I knocked full measure.
F
Some they offered fame and pleasure,
E^m
But I found life's greatest treasure
F G G^7 C
when the love came a tum-ba-lin' down.

2. Life is a long hard journey and
To Him it matters where it ends
So make the journey count my friend
And Love will come a tum-ba-lin' down.

3. I know that the Lord is with us.
I know that the Lord is with us.
I know that the Lord is with us
and the love will come a tum-ba-lin' down.

4. I know for the Lord has shown me.
I know for the Lord has shown me.
I know for the Lord has shown me
and the love will come a tum-ba-lin' down.

5. I know for the Lord has told me.
I know for the Lord has told me.
I know for the Lord has told me
and the love will come a tum-ba-lin' down.

GO, TELL IT ON THE MOUNTAIN 66

Traditional Spiritual

Chorus:

```
 F          B♭      F          C7                    F     C
Go, tell it on the mountain, Over the hills and everywhere;
 F  B♭              F                       Gm C7   F
Go, tell it on the mountain That Jesus Christ is born.
```

```
                          C          F
1.    While shepherds kept their watching
             C7    Dm   C7     F
      O'er silent flocks by night,
                        C          F
      Behold, throughout the heavens
                 Gm      G7  C7
      There shone a holy light.

      (Chorus)
```

2. The shepherds feared and trembled
When, lo! above the earth
Rang out the angel chorus
That hailed our Savior's birth.

(Chorus)

3. Down in a lowly manger
Our humble Christ was born,
And God sent us salvation
That blessed Christmas morn.

(Chorus)

67 WHAT CHILD IS THIS, WHO, LAID TO REST

Traditional English carol
Adapt. by William C. Dix, c. 1865

Greensleeves 8 7 8 7 Ref.
Traditional English melody, 16th century

Em G D
1. **What Child is this, who, laid to rest,**
Em Am B B7
On Mary's lap is sleeping?
Em G D
Whom angels greet with anthems sweet,
Em Am Em
While shepherds watch are keeping?

Chorus:
Bm G D
This, this is Christ the King,
B Em Am B B7
Whom shepherds guard and angels sing:
Bm G D
This, this is Christ the King,
B Em B Em
The babe, the Son of Mary.

2. **Why lies He in such mean estate**
Where ox and ass are feeding?
Good Christian, fear; for sinners here
The silent Word is pleading.

(Chorus)

3. **So bring Him incense, gold and myrrh,**
Come, peasant, king, to own Him;
The King of kings salvation brings,
Let loving hearts enthrone Him.

(Chorus)

O COME, ALL YE FAITHFUL

Latin hymn
Attr. to John F. Wade, 1751
Trans. by Frederick Oakeley, 1841, and others

Adeste Fideles Irreg. Ref.
John F. Wade's Cantus Diversi, 1751

Capo 1

```
     G                        D        G  D   G  C  G   D
1.   O come, all ye faithful, joyful and triumphant,
     Em        D  A D G  D G D  A7  D
     O come ye, O come ye to Bethlehem!
       G   D7  G  D7  G     D   G  Em   Am  D
     Come and behold Him, born the King of angels;
```

Chorus:

```
 G         D7 G D7 G         G         D7  G  D7 G  D7
O come, let us adore Him, O come, let us adore Him,
 G D7    G D7 C D7  G C  G D7  G
O come, let us adore Him, Christ the Lord.
```

2. God of God, and Light of Light begotten,
Lo, He abhors the Virgin's womb;
Very God, begotten, not created;

(Chorus)

3. Sing, choirs of angels, sing in exultation!
O sing, all ye citizens of heav'n above;
Glory to God, all glory in the highest;

(Chorus)

4. Yea, Lord, we greet thee, born this happy morning,
Jesus, to Thee be all glory giv'n;
Word of the Father, now in flesh appearing;

(Chorus)

69 WHO IS HE IN YONDER STALL?

Words and Music by Benjamin R. Hanby

Capo 2

Chorus:

```
 G  D7   G          C    G      D
'Tis the Lord!  oh wondrous story!
D7                             G
'Tis the Lord!  the King of glory!
                            C
At His feet we humbly fall
                G        D      D7     G
Crown Him!  crown Him,  Lord of all!
```

```
          G                        C
1.    Who is He in yonder stall,
                  G          A7          D  D7
      At whose feet the shepherds fall?
```

(Chorus)

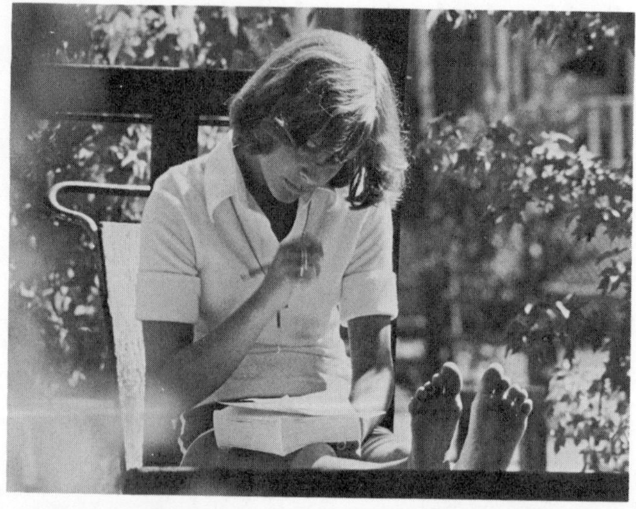

2. Who is He in deep distress
Fasting in the wilderness?
(Chorus)

3. Who is He the people bless
For his words of gentleness?
(Chorus)

4. Who is He to whom they bring
All the sick and sorrowing?
(Chorus)

5. Who is He that stands and weeps
At the grave where Lazarus sleeps?
(Chorus)

6. Who is He the gathering throng
Greet with loud triumphant song?
(Chorus)

7. Lo! at midnight, who is He
Prays in dark Gethsemane?
(Chorus)

8. Who is He on yonder tree
Dies in grief and agony?
(Chorus)

9. Who is He who from the grave
Comes to succour, help, and save?
(Chorus)

10. Who is He who from His throne
Rules through all the worlds alone?
(Chorus)

70 JOY TO THE WORLD! THE LORD IS COME

Words by Isaac Watts
Based on Psalm 98

Music by George Frederick Handel
Arr. by Lowell Mason

D G D E^m D A^7 D
1. Joy to the world! the Lord is come;
G A^7 D
Let earth receive her King;
G D G D
Let every heart prepare Him room,
And heav'n and nature sing,
A A^7
And heav'n and nature sing,
D G D G D A^7 D
And heav'n, and heav'n and nature sing.

2. Joy to the earth! the Savior reigns;
Let men their songs employ;
While fields and floods, rocks, hills, and plains
Repeat the sounding joy,
Repeat the sounding joy,
Repeat, repeat the sounding joy.

3. No more let sins and sorrows grow,
Nor thorns infest the ground;
He comes to make His blessings flow
Far as the curse is found,
Far as the curse is found,
Far as, far as the curse is found.

4. He rules the world with truth and grace,
And makes the nations prove
The glories of His righteousness,
And wonders of His love,
And wonders of His love,
And wonders, and wonders of His love.

SILENT NIGHT! HOLY NIGHT! 71

Words by Joseph Mohr
Trans. by John F. Young

Stille Nacht Irreg.
Franz Gruber

Capo 3

G D^7 G
1. Silent night! Holy night! All is calm, all is bright
C G
'Round yon virgin mother and Child,
C G
Holy Infant so tender and mild,
D^7 G D D^7 G
Sleep in heavenly peace, Sleep in heavenly peace.

2. Silent night! Holy night!
Shepherds quake at the sight,
Glories stream from heaven afar,
Heav'nly hosts sing Alleluia;
Christ the Savior is born, Christ the Savior is born.

3. Silent night! Holy night!
Son of God, love's pure light,
Radiant beams from Thy holy face,
With the dawn of redeeming grace,
Jesus, Lord, at Thy birth, Jesus, Lord, at Thy birth.

AWAY IN A MANGER 72

Words by Martin Luther
Music by Carl Mueller

F B♭ F
1. Away in a manger, No crib for His bed,
C^7 F
The little Lord Jesus Laid down His sweet head,
F B♭ F
The stars in the sky Looked down where He lay,
C^7 F G^m C^7 F
The little Lord Jesus, Asleep on the hay.

2. The cattle are lowing, The poor Baby wakes,
But little Lord Jesus, No crying He makes.
I love Thee, Lord Jesus, Look down from the sky,
And stay by my side Until morning is nigh.

73 LORD OF THE DANCE

Words by Sydney Carter
Tune traditiona, arr. and
adapted by Sydney Carter

Chorus:

Bm Em Bm Em
Dance then wherever you may be;
G C D
I am the Lord of the Dance, said He,
G Em Bm G7
I'll lead you all wherever you may be,
C D7 G C G
I will lead you all in the Dance, said He.

G Bm Em
1. I danced in the morning when the world was begun,
C Am7 D7
And I danced in the moon and the stars and the sun,
G Em
And I came down from heaven
Bm Em
and I danced on the earth,
C D7 G C G
At Bethlehem I had my birth.

(Chorus)

2. I danced for the scribe and the Pharisee,
But they would not dance
and they wouldn't follow me,
I danced for the fisherman, for James and for John,
They came with me and the dance went on.

(Chorus)

3. I danced on the Sabbath and I cured the lame,
The holy people, they said it was a shame,
They whipped and they stripped
and they hung me high,
And they left me there on a cross to die.

(Chorus)

4. I danced on a Friday when the sky turned black,
It's hard to dance with the devil on your back,
They buried my body and they thought I'd gone,
But I am the dance and I still go on.

(Chorus)

5. They cut me down and I leap up high.
I am the life that'll never, never die,
I'll live in you if you'll live in me,
I am the Lord of the Dance, said He.

(Chorus)

74 AT SEVENTEEN

Words and Music by Janis Ian

C
1. I learned the truth at seventeen
D^m
That love was meant for beauty queens
G^7
and high school girls with clear-skinned smiles
C
who married young and then retired.
C
The valentines I never knew,
D^m
the Friday night charades of youth
G^7
were spent on one more beautiful
C
At seventeen I learned the truth.
E♭
And those of us with ravaged faces,
D^{m7} G^7
Lacking in the social graces,
C^{m7} F^{m7}
Desperately remained at home
C^{m7} F^{m7}
inventing lovers on the phone.
A♭ G^7
Who called to say, "Come dance with me,"
C^{m7} F^{m7}
and murmured vague obscenities.
D^{m7} G^7
It isn't all it seems at seventeen.

2. A brown-eyed girl in hand-me-downs
whose name I never could pronounce
said, "Pity, please, the ones who serve
they only get what they deserve.
The rich relationed hometown queen
marries into what she needs
A guarantee of company
And haven for the elderly."
Remember those who win the game
lose the love they sought to gain
In debentures of quality and dubious integrity.
Their small town eyes will gape at you
in dull surprise when payment due
exceeds accounts received at seventeen.

3. To those of us who know the pain
of valentines that never came,
and those whose names were never called
when choosing sides for basketball.
It was long ago and far away.
The world was younger than today
and dreams were all they gave for free
to ugly duckling girls like me.
We all play the game and when we dare
to cheat ourselves at solitaire
Inventing lovers on the phone,
repenting other lives unknown.
that call and say, "Come dance with me"
and murmur vague obscenities
at ugly girls like me at seventeen.

75 WHAT A FRIEND WE HAVE IN JESUS

Words by Joseph Scriven
Music by Charles C. Converse

F B♭ F F7 B♭
1. What a friend we have in Jesus,
F C
All our sins and griefs to bear;
F B♭ F F7 B♭
What a privilege to carry
F Gm F C7 F
Everything to God in prayer!
C C7 F
O what peace we often forfeit,
B♭ F C7 F C
O what needless pain we bear,
F B♭ F B♭
All because we do not carry
F Gm F C7 F
Everything to God in prayer.

2. Have we trials and temptations?
Is there trouble anywhere?
We should never be discouraged;
Take it to the Lord in prayer.
Can we find a friend so faithful,
Who will all our sorrows share?
Jesus knows our every weakness;
Take it to the Lord in prayer.

3. Are we weak and heavy laden,
Cumbered with a load of care?
Precious Savior, still our refuge;
Take it to the Lord in prayer.
Do thy friends despise, forsake thee?
Take it to the Lord in prayer;
In His arms He'll take and shield thee,
Thou wilt find a solace there.

FIRE ON THE MOUNTAIN TONIGHT 76

Words and Music by Randy Palmer

Chorus:

G C G
There's a fire on the mountain tonight.
G D
There's no place to run, no place to hide.
C D^7 E^m C
Tell me now, would you be alright if you had to die tonight?
G/D D G
There's a fire on the mountain tonight.

G C G
1. Moses, he led the pack.
G D
And once he started out, no turning back.
C D^7
With old Pharoah at his heels,
E^m C
the Red Sea began to swell,
G/D D G
and he crossed to the other side safe and dry.

2. Elijah, he cried out from the trees.
He said, "You're living life in sin and misery."
They said, "Hey, buddy, you must be blind,
'cause we're all having a good time."
But Elijah bowed his head and cried from grief.

3. Simon Peter, he denied our Lord
Three times and finally he swore.
Then the cock began to crow, and he said,
"How did He know?"
And from that moment Peter was a rock.

4. Jesus, He died upon the cross.
And for our sins He paid the cost.
Now He's inviting you to choose,
it's your chance to win or lose,
But it's your decision, your gain or loss.

77 ABILENE

Arr. by John D. Loudermilk, Lester Brown & Bob Gibson

Chorus:

G B7
Abilene, — Abilene
C G
Prettiest town I've ever seen —
A7 D7
Women there — don't treat you mean —
G C G Am7 D7
In Abilene, my Abilene.

G
1. I sit alone
B7
Most ev'ry night
C
Watch those trains
G
Pull out of sight
A7 D7 G
Don't I wish they were carrying me back to Abilene,
C G
My Abilene.

(Chorus)

2. Crowded city
There ain't nothing free
Nothing in this town for me
Wish to the Lord
that I could be in Abilene, sweet Abilene.

(Chorus)

TURN IT OVER

78

By Noel Stookey and Ed Mottau

Chorus:

```
                    C               G                  F                G
Well, turn it over to the Father — turn it over to the Son
                    C              Esus4        E7
Well, turn it over in the Spirit (um hoo-boo)
Am          D7              G  (G C G)
Till the Kingdom come
                    C               G                  F                G  (G C G)
Well, turn it over to the Father — turn it over to the Son
                    C              Esus4        E7
Well, turn it over in the Spirit (um hoo)
  Am          D7           G  (G C G)
Until the kingdom come.
```

```
              Bm                      G
1.    Well, deep in the woods the sound of an axe
        C                            A7
      Clearing the field by the sweat of his back
          G                     Bm7
      A man of the soil plants his seeds
           C                              A7
      And prays that the earth will provide what he needs,

      He turns it . . .
```

2. And out on the street there's a kid left for dead
From playing with things that put holes in his head.
A visiting minister in from the sticks
Reads from the Bible
And here's what he picks.

3. In the front seat of a bus from Birmingham
A man with a smile reads that letter again.
Come home, Pop, the struggle is through
When we heard you found Jesus, well,
We decided to . . .

79 AND CAN IT BE

Words by Charles Wesley
Music by Thomas Campbell

```
              G        D7          D7    G
Chorus:    Amazing love!  How can it be
                  C          G       C        G   D7 G
           That Thou, my God, shouldst die for me!

              G       D G     C   D     G
   1.        And can it be that I should gain
                C   D  Em       A7      D
             An interest in the Saviour's blood?
              G   D   G  D7        G         D7
             Died He for me, who caused His pain,
                  C        G             D7 G
             For me, who Him to death pursued?
             G   D7    G          C  A D
             Amazing love!  How can it be
                   G      C            D      G
             That Thou, my God, shouldst die for me?
```

2. 'Tis mystery all! Th'Immortal dies!
Who can explore His strange design?
In vain the firstborn seraph tries
To sound the depths of love divine!
'Tis mercy all! Let earth adore;
Let angel minds inquire no more.

3. He left His Father's throne above,
So free, so infinite His grace;
Emptied Himself of all but love,
And bled for Adam's helpless race,
'Tis mercy all, immense and free!
For, O my God, it found out me.

4. Long my imprisoned spirit lay
Fastbound in sin and nature's night;
Thine eye diffused a quickening ray.
I woke, the dungeon flamed with light;
My chains fell off, my heart was free;
I rose, went forth, and followed Thee.

5. No condemnation now I dread;
Jesus, and all in Him, is mine!
Alive in Him, my living Head,
And clothed in righteousness divine,
Bold I approach the eternal throne,
And claim the crown through Christ, my own.

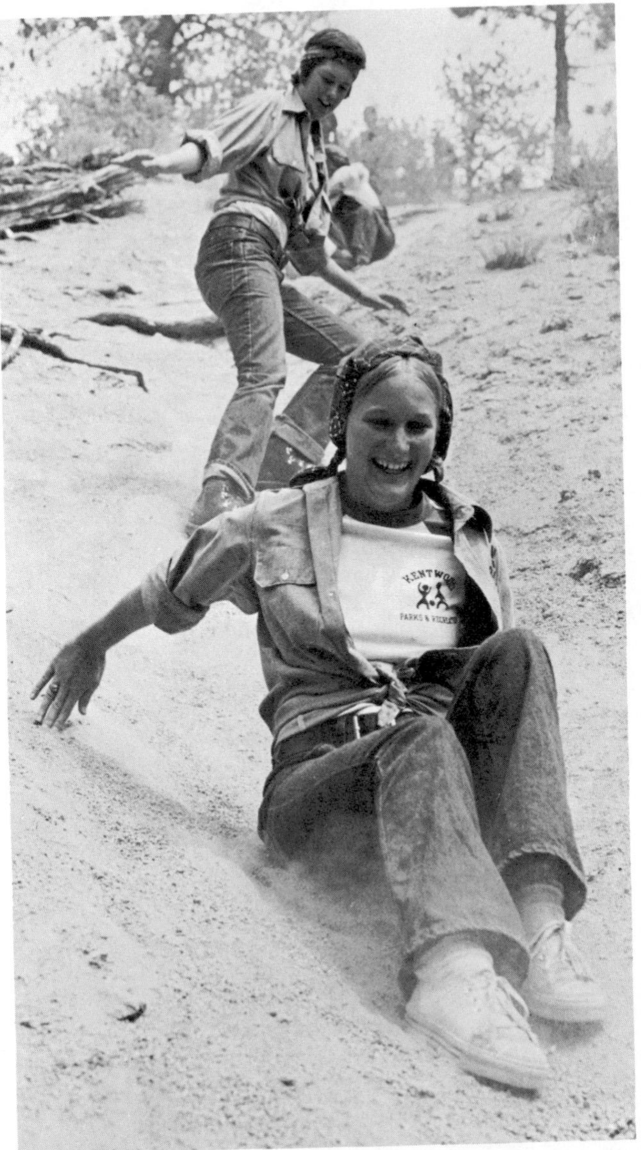

80 GAMES PEOPLE PLAY

Words and Music by Joe South

Chorus:

```
 F
La, da, da, da, da, da, da.
                  C
La, da, da, da, da, da, dee.
                 B♭       C                          F
Talkin' 'bout you and me, and the games people play.
```

```
1.    F
      Oh, the games people play now,
                                C
      Ev'ry night and ev'ry day, now.
                                  B
      Never meanin' what they say, now.
        C                      F
      Never sayin' what they mean.

      And they while away the hours
                           C
      in their ivory towers,
                                      B
      'Til they're covered up with flowers,
                 C                     F
      In the back of a black limousine.
```

(Chorus)

2. Oh, we make one another cry;
Break a heart then we say goodbye;
Cross our hearts and we hope to die.
That the other was to blame.
Neither one will ever give in.
So, we gaze at an eight by ten,
Thinkin' 'bout the things that might have been
It's a dirty rotten shame.

(Chorus)

3. People walkin' up to you,
Singin' Glory Hallelujah!
And they're try'n' to sock it to you.
In the name of the Lord.
They gonna teach you how to meditate;
Read your horoscope, cheat your fate,
And furthermore to hell with hate
Come on get on board.

(Chorus)

4. Look around, tell me what you see
What's happenin' to you and me.
God grant me the serenity,
To remember who I am.
'Cause you're givin' up your sanity
For your pride and your vanity,
Turn your back on humanity.
And you don't give a da, da, da, da, da.

(Chorus)

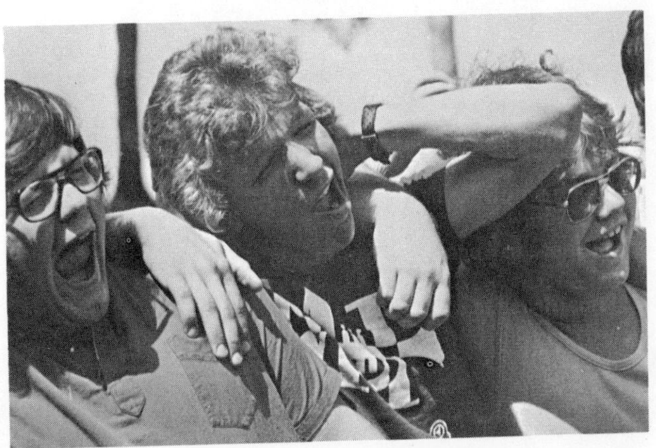

81 BLESS HIS HOLY NAME

Words and Music by Andrae Crouch

D A7 D A7 D G9 G
Bless the Lord, oh, my soul, and all that is within me;
A Bm A7 D (G D A7)
Bless His Holy name.
D A7 D A7 D G9 G
Bless the Lord, oh, my soul, and all that is within me;
A Bm A7 D (G D A7)
Bless His Holy name.
D E9 A7 D
He has done great things, He has done great things;
D D7 G Em7 D A7 D
He has done great things, bless His Holy name.
D A7 D A7 D G9 G
Bless the Lord, oh, my soul, and all that is within me;
A Bm A7 Bm Gm7 Bm7 Em7 A7 D
Bless His Holy name. Bless His Holy name.

PROUD MARY

Words and Music by J. C. Fogerty

(Chorus)

```
 D                       Em
Big wheel keep on turnin', Proud Mary keep on burnin',
  G
Rollin', rollin', rollin' on the river.
```

```
       G
1.     Left a good job in the city,
```

Workin' for The Man ev'ry night and day,

And I never lost one minute of sleepin,'

Worryin' 'bout the way things might have been.

(Chorus)

2. **If you come down to the river,**
Bet you gonna find some people who live.
You don't have to worry 'cause you have no money,
People on the river are happy to give.

(Chorus)

3. **Cleaned a lot of plates in Memphis,**
Pumped a lot of pain in New Orleans,
But I never saw the good side of the city,
Until I hitched a ride on a river boat queen.

(Chorus)

83 I AM THE LIGHT OF THE WORLD

Words* and Music by Jim Strathdee

*In response to a Christmas poem by Howard Thurman

Chorus:

B♭(F) C(G) F(C)
"I am the light of the world!
B♭(F) C(G) F(C)
You people come and follow me!"
Gm(Dm) Dm(Am) C(G) F(C) B♭(F)
If you follow and love You'll learn the mystery
Gm(Dm) C(G) B♭(F) F(C)
of what you were meant to do and be.

1. F(C) B♭(F) C(G) F(C)
When the song of the angels is stilled,
Gm(Dm) Dm(Am) C(G)
When the star in the sky is gone,
F(C) B♭(F)
When the kings and the shepherds
C(G) F(C)
have found their way home,
Dm(Am) B♭(F) C (G)
The work of Christmas is begun:

2. **To find the lost and the lonely man,**
To heal his broken soul with love,
To feed the hungry children
with warmth and good food,
To feel the earth below the sky above!

3. **To free the pris'ner from his chains,**
To make the powerful care,
To rebuild the nations with strength of good will,
To call a man your brother ev'ry where!

4. **To bring hope to ev'ry task you do,**
To dance at a baby's new birth,
To make music in an old man's heart,
And sing to the colors of the earth!

WILL THE CIRCLE BE UNBROKEN?

Words and Music by A. P. Carter

Chorus:

G G^7
Will the circle be unbroken
C G
Bye and bye, Lord, bye and bye;
G
There's a better home awaiting,
G D^7 G
in the sky, Lord, in the sky.

G G^7
1. I was standin' by my window
C G
On one cold and cloudy day,
G
When I saw this hearse come rollin'
G D^7 G
For to carry my mother away.

(Chorus)

2. Lord, I told the undertaker
Undertaker, please drive slow;
For this body you are hauling
Lord, I hate to see her go.

(Chorus)

3. I will follow close behind her
Try to hold off and be brave
But I could not hide my sorrow
When they laid her in her grave.

(Chorus)

4. I went home, Lord, my home was lonesome,
Miss my mother, she was gone;
All my brothers, sisters crying,
What a home so sad and lorn.

(Chorus)

85 LEAN ON ME

Words and Music by Bill Winters

G Am Bm C Bm Am G Am Bm D7
Sometimes in our lives, we all have pain, we all have sorrow.
G Am Bm C Bm Am G Am Bm D7 G
But, if we are wise, we know that there's always tomorrow.
G Am Bm C Bm Am G
Lean on me, when you're not strong and I'll be your friend
Am Bm D7 G Am Bm C
I'll help you carry on for it won't be long
Bm Am G Am Bm D7 G
'til I'm gonna need somebody to lean on.
G Am Bm C
Please swallow your pride
Bm Am G Am Bm D7
If I have things you need to borrow
G Am Bm C Bm Am G
for no one can fill those of your needs
Am Bm D7 G
that you won't let show.

You just call on me, brother, when you need a hand,

We all need somebody to lean on,

I just might have a problem that you'll understand,
D7 G
We all need somebody to lean on.
G Am Bm C Bm Am G
Lean on me when you're not strong and I'll be your friend,
Am Bm D7 G Am Bm C
I'll help you carry on. For it won't be long
Bm Am G D G
'til I'm gonna need somebody to lean on.

(Repeat)

G   Am   Bm   C   Bm Am G   Am Bm D7
If there is a load you have to bear that you can't carry,

G   Am Bm C   Bm   Am   G
I'm right up the road, I'll share your load

Am Bm D7 G   Am G   Am   G
If you just call me — call me (if you need a friend) call me.

ALL DAY SONG 86

Words and Music by John Fischer

C   G   Am7   G
Love Him in the mornin' when you see the sun arisin'.

C   G   Am7   G
Love Him in the evenin' cause He took you through the day.

C   G   Am7
And in the in-between time when you feel

G
The pressure comin',

C   G   Am7   G
Remember that He loves you and He promises to stay.

D   G
When you think you got to worry

D   G
'Cause it seems the thing to do;

D   Em   C   D
Remember He ain't in a hurry, He's always got time for you.

87 MOTHER NATURE'S SON

Words and Music by John Lennon and Paul McCartney

B♭/C   E♭/F   B♭/C
1. Born a poor young country boy,
E♭/F   F/B   Gm/Cm C7/D7
Mother Nature's son,
F/B B♭6/C F/B B♭/C F/B
All day long I'm sitting
B♭/C   F/B   F11   B♭/C B♭m7/Cm7 E♭/F B
singing songs for ev'ryone.

2. Sit beside a mountain stream,
See her waters rise;
Listen to the pretty sound
of music as she flies.
B   B   E   B
Du du du du du du du du du du
B   B   E   B   B♭11 B♭7 E B
Du du du du du du du du du du du du du.

3. Find me in my field of grass,
Mother Nature's son.
Swaying daisies sing a lazy song
beneath the sun.
B   B♭m7 E   B
Hm hm Mother Nature's son.

DAY BY DAY 88

Words by Lina Sandell Berg
Trans. by Andrew L. Skoog
Music by Oscar Ahnfelt

Em G7 C C7 F Dm
1. **Day by day and with each passing moment,**
G7 C
Strength I find to meet my trials here;
Em G7 C C7 F Dm
Trusting in my Father's wise bestowment,
G7 C
I've no cause for worry or for fear.
F
He whose heart is kind beyond all measure
G Em G7 C
Gives unto each day what He deems best —
Em G7 C C7 F Dm
Lovingly, its part of pain and pleasure,
G7 C
Mingling toil with peace and rest.

2. **Ev'ry day the Lord Himself is near me**
With a special mercy for each hour;
All my cares He fain would bear, and cheer me,
He whose name is Counselor and Pow'r.
The protection of His child and treasure
Is a charge that on Himself He laid;
"As thy days, thy strength shall be in measure,"
This the pledge to me He made.

3. **Help me then in ev'ry tribulation**
So to trust Thy promises, O Lord,
That I lose not faith's sweet consolation
Offered me within Thy holy word.
Help me, Lord, when toil and trouble meeting,
E'er to take, as from a father's hand,
One by one, the day's, the moments fleeting,
Till I reach the promised land.

89 CAUSE ME TO HEAR

Words and Music by Jim Moore
Psalm 143:8

G A^m D
Cause me to hear Thy lovingkindness in the morning,
D G
Cause me to know the way wherein I should walk,
G^7 C C^m
For I lift up my soul unto Thee, O Lord,
G/D D^7 G
And in Thee do I trust all the day.

90 JOSHUA

Traditional

Chorus:

E^m A^m E^m
Joshua fit the battle of Jericho, Jericho, Jericho-o-o,
E^m
Joshua fit the battle of Jericho,
E^m E^m D C
And the walls came a-tum-bal-in' down, down, down.
B^7 E^m D C B^7
shu, be, du, be; down, down, down, down.

E^m
1. You may talk about your men of Gideon,
B^7
You may talk about your men of Saul;
E^m
But there's none like good old Joshua
E^m E^m B^7
at the battle of Jericho, Oh.

2. (Chorus)
Right up to the walls of Jericho,
He marched with spear in hand;
Old Joshua commanded the children to SHOUT,
(slow) **And the walls came a tumblin' down.**
That morning . . . .

(Chorus) Last chorus slow. Blues beat.

(Ending) And the walls came tumblin' down
Joshua *(whisper)*

15

91 CAT'S IN THE CRADLE

Words and Music by Harry Chapin and Sandy Chapin

Capo 1

Chorus:

E D
And the cat's in the cradle and the silver spoon,
G A
Little boy blue and the man in the moon.
E
"When you comin' home Dad?" (Son?)
D G Bm/F# E
"I don't know when, but we'll get together then;
G Bm/F# E
You know we'll have a good time then."

1. E G
My child arrived just the other day;
A E
He came to the world in the usual way.
G
But there were planes to catch and bills to pay;
A E
He learned to walk while I was away.
D D/C#
And he was talkin' 'fore I knew it,
Bm7 D/A G Bm/F# E
And as he grew he'd say, "I'm gonna be like you, Dad,
G Bm/F# E
you know I'm gonna be like you."

(Chorus)

2. My son turned ten just the other day;
he said, "Thanks for the ball, Dad, come on let's play.
Can you teach me to throw?" I said, "Not today,
I got a lot to do." He said, "That's okay."
And he, he walked away,
but his smile never dimmed, it said,
"I'm gonna be like him, yeah,
you know I'm gonna be like him."

(Chorus)

3. Well, he came from college just the other day;
so much like a man I just had to say,
"Son, I'm proud of you, can you sit for awhile?"
He shook his head and he said with a smile,
"What I'd really like, Dad, is to borrow the car keys;
See you later, can I have them please?"

(Chorus)

4. I've long since retired, my son's moved away;
I called him up just the other day.
I said, "I'd like to see you if you don't mind."
He said, "I'd love to, Dad, if I can find the time.
You see, my new job's a hassle and the kids have the flu,
but it's sure nice talkin' to you, Dad,
it's been sure nice talkin' to you."
And as I hung up the phone, it occurred to me,
he'd grown up just like me; my boy was just like me.

(Chorus)

DO YOU KNOW WHERE YOU'RE GOING TO?

Words by Gerry Goffin
Music by Michael Masser

C F
Do you know where you're going to?
Dm E7 Am
Do you like the things that life is showing you?
Dm E7 A
Where are you going to, do you know?
C F
Do you get what you're hoping for?
Dm E7 Am
When you look behind you there's no open door.
Dm E7 A
What are you hoping for, do you know?
B E F#
Once we were standing still in time,
Bm Dmaj7 E7 D E7 A D A
Chasing the fantasies that filled our minds.
A B7 G#m7 C#m7
And you knew how I loved you but my spirit was free,
F#m Amaj7 A B7 D E D
Laughing at the questions that you once asked of me.
C F
Do you know where you're going to?
Dm E7 Am
Do you like the things that life is showing you?
Dm E7 A
Where are you going to, do you know?
A B E F#
Now, looking back at all we planned,
Bm Dmaj7 E7 D E7 A D A
We let so many dreams just slip through our hands.
A B G#m C#m
Why must we wait so long before we see
F#m Amaj7 A B7 D E E7
how sad the answers to those questions can be?

C F
Do you know where you're going to?
D^m E^7 A^m
Do you like the things that life is showing you?
D^m E^7 A
Where you are going to, do you know?
C F
Do you get what you're hoping for?
D^m E^7 A^m
When you look behind you there's no open door.
D^m E^7 A
What are you hoping for, do you know?

93 GOODBYE AGAIN

Words and Music by John Denver

Chorus:

```
                 Em    A7          D    D/C#    Bm
And it's goodbye again, I'm sorry to be leaving you
       Em    A7   D      D/C#        Bm              Em   A7
goodbye again, 'cause if you didn't know it's goodbye again
    D         D/C#   Bm         Em
And I wish you could tell me why do we always fight
                A7
when I have to go?
```

```
             D    D/C#        Bm             G           D
1.   It's five o'clock this mornin' and the sun is on the rise
                   D      D/C#   Bm
     There's frosting on the window pane
         Em               A7
     and sorrow in your eyes
          D        D/C#     Bm        G            D
     The stars are fading quietly the night is nearly gone
         D     D/C#       Bm
     and so you turn away from me
         Em              A7
     and tears begin to come.
```

(Chorus)

2. It seems a shame to leave you now,
the days are soft and warm.
I long to lay me down again and hold you in my arms
I long to kiss the tears away
and give you back your smile,
But other voices beckon me — for a little while.

F♯m G
3. I have to go and see some friends of mine
D D/C♯ Bm
Some that I don't know and
Em A7 D
Some who aren't familiar with my name.
F♯m G
It's something that's inside of me
D D/C♯ Bm
not hard to understand,
Em A7
It's anyone who'll listen to me sing.

4. And if your arms are empty now who am I to blame.
You think if I were always here
our love would be the same.
As it is the time we have is worth the time alone
And lying by your side
the greatest peace I've ever known. And it's

(Chorus)

94 YOU'RE THE ONE

Words and Music by Cindy Wheeler

Chorus:

```
            F   G             C
'Cause You - You're the One –
  F                 Dm              G          C
You make me feel like my life's just begun –
       F   G             C
And You – You're the One –
       F             Em                 Dm          G
My life's in your hands now there's no need to run,
               C F G
You're the One.
```

```
            C                F            G           C
1.      Lord, there are times when I am confused –
                 Am         G          F          G
        and I haven't a clue what it is I should do.
             C              F         G         C
        But just like the sun – after the rain
        Am              G                F        G
        I know that you will shine on me again.
            C                F              G         C
        And I used to think I could make it alone –
            Am        G      F              G
        that I'd get along if I could be strong.
             C               F              G         C
        But just like a child that's lost in a storm,
            Am                G         F               G
        I needed your rescue to keep me from harm.
```

(Chorus)

```
        C             F              G          C
2.      I couldn't live now like I did before.
           Am              G      F               G
        No it wouldn't do to live without You,
               C             F                G          C
        For Your love is constant and I have no fear.
             Am     G               F                G
        Wherever I am I know You're always near.
```

(Chorus)

```
                      C F G     G          C F G G C C
        You're the One – You're the One.
```

I'M IN LOVE WITH A BIG BLUE FROG

By Les Braunstein

1. E
I'm in love with a big blue frog,
E B^7
a big blue frog loves me.
E E^7 A G
It's not as bad as it appears,
E B^7 E B
he wears glasses and he's six foot three.
E
Well, I'm not worried about our kids,
E B^7
I know they'll turn out neat,
E E^7 A G
They'll be great lookin' 'cause they'll have my face,
E B^7 E B
great swimmers 'cause they'll have his feet.

2. Well, I'm in love with a big blue frog,
a big blue frog loves me.
He's not as bad as he appears,
he's got rhythm and a P.H.D.
Well, I know we can make things work,
he's got good family sense,
His mother was a frog from Philadelphia,
his daddy an enchanted prince.

3. (Instrumental)
The neighbors are against it and it's clear to me
and it's probably clear to you,
They think values on their property will go right down
if the family next door is blue.

4. Well, I'm in love with a big blue frog,
a big blue frog loves me.
I've got it tattooed on my chest, it says:
E B^7 E C♯ $F♯^7$ B^7 E E^7 A G° E
P.H.R.O.G. it's frog to me, P. H. R. O. G.

96 NOW LET US SING

Traditional

Start Slow Repeat a little faster each time.

```
                          A
Group 1:  Now let us sing;

Group 2:  Sing to the power of the Lord come down.
                          A
Group 1:  Now let us sing;
                                        E
Group 2:  Sing to the power of the Lord come down.
                             A
Group 1:  Lift up your voice,
                            A7
Group 2:  Lift up your voice,
                     D
Group 1:  Be not afraid,

Group 2:  Be not afraid,
                          A
Group 1:  Now let us sing,
                                         E7        A
1 and 2:  Sing to the power of the Lord come down.
```

97 JESUS IS THE LIGHT

Traditional

Arranged by Yohann Anderson

```
G
Jesus is the light,

He's the light of the world.  Bom, Bom, Bom:
 D7
Jesus is the light,
            G
He's the light of the world.  Bom, Bom, Bom:

Jesus is the light,
                          C
He's the light of the world.
          G   D7               G
And he's ever shinin in my soul.
```

WADE IN THE WATER

Traditional

Chorus:

```
Em                         B7   Em
Wade, wade, wade in the water.
Em                         B7   Em
Wade, wade, wade in the water.
Em
Wade in the water.  (You got to)
              Am      B7
Wade in the water, Children.
Em
Wade in the water.
                               B7  Em
The Lord's gonna trouble the water.
```

```
         Em
1.       Who's that yonder dressed in red?
                                  B7 Em
         Wade, wade, wade in the water.
         Em
         Must be the children that Moses led.
                                  B7 Em
         Wade, wade, wade in the water.  (You got to)
```

(Chorus)

2. Who's that yonder dressed in white,
   Wade, wade, wade in the water.
   Must be the children of the Israelites,
   Wade in the water.

(Chorus)

3. Who's that yonder dressed in green,
   Wade, wade, wade in the water.
   Must be the hypocrites turning mean,
   Wade in the water.

(Chorus)

Adapted and arranged by Yohann Anderson 1972

99 COTTON FIELDS

Traditional

E
When I was a little bitty baby my mama would
A E B^7
Rock me in the cradle in them old cotton fields back home
E
When I was a little bitty baby my mama would
A E B^7 E
Rock me in the cradle in them old cotton fields back home.
A
And when them cotton balls get rotten
E
You can't pick very much cotton
B^7
In them old cotton fields back home.
E A E
It was down in Louisiana just about a mile from Texarkana
B^7 E
In them old cotton fields back home.

WHEN WILL I BE LOVED? 100

Words and Music by Phil Everly

I've been cheated, been mistreated, when will I be loved?
F B♭ C F B♭ C
I've been pushed down, I've been pushed 'round,
F B♭ C F
When will I be loved?
B♭ C B♭ F
When I find my new man that I want for mine,
B♭ C Dm C
He always breaks my heart in two – it happens ev'rytime.
F B♭ C F B♭ C F B♭ C F
I've been made blue, I've been lied to; when will I be loved?
B♭ C B♭ F
When I find my new man that I want for mine,
B♭ C Dm C
He always breaks my heart in two – it happens ev'rytime.
F B♭ C F B♭ C F B♭ C F
I've been cheated, been mistreated; when will I be loved?
F B♭ C F B♭
When will I be loved?
C F
Tell me, when will I be loved?

101 DO LORD! (PSALM 27)

Traditional American

Arr. by J. Ylvisaker
Paraphrase by J.Y.

Chorus:

G
Do Lord, O do Lord, O do remember me!
C G
Do Lord, O do Lord, O do remember me!
G B7 Em
Do Lord, O do Lord, O do remember me!
Am7 D7 G
Look away beyond the blue!

G
1. **You're my light and my salvation, I won't be afraid!**
C
You're the stronghold of my life,
G
by You all things were made.
G B7 Em
Foes attack me, hassle me, but I will never fade,
Am7 D7 G
For I move in the strength of the Lord.

(Chorus)

2. **Though a host encamp against me, I will never fear!**
Even though a war surrounds me You are always near.
One thing I have asked of You that I will seek for sure,
Is to live in the house of the Lord.

(Chorus)

3. You will hide me in Your shelter in the day of strife;
You'll conceal me in Your tent
or set me on the height.
Now my head is lifted up above the storms of night,
So I'll sing in the name of the Lord.

(Chorus)

4. Glory be to God the Father and to God the Son;
Glory be to God the Spirit, ever Three in One.
As it was in the beginning till our race is won,
We can live in the light of the Lord.

(Chorus)

5. I've got a home in Gloryland that outshines the sun.
I've got a home in Gloryland that outshines the sun.
I've got a home in Gloryland that outshines the sun.
Look away beyond the blue!

(Chorus)

6. I took Jesus as my Savior you take Him too.
I took Jesus as my Savior you take Him too.
I took Jesus as my Savior you take Him too.
Look away beyond the blue.

(Chorus)

102 THAT'LL BE THE DAY

Words and Music by Norman Petty, Buddy Holly and Jerry Allison

Chorus:

```
          B♭
Well, that'll be the day, when you say goodbye.
    F
That'll be the day, when you make me cry.
   B♭
You say you're gonna leave me; you know it's a lie,
        F                    C    F
'Cause that'll be the day when I die.
```

```
                  B♭
1.   Well, you gave me all your lovin'
                F
     and your turtle-dovin',
       B♭                         F
     All your hugs and kisses and your money too.
     B
     You know you love me, baby;
     F                         G7
     Still you tell me, baby, that some day, well,
     C7
     I'll be through.
```

(Chorus)

2. **When Cupid shot his dart,**
he shot it at your heart.
So if we ever part and I leave you,
you kiss and hold me and you
tell me boldly,
Well, that some day, well,
I'll be through.

(Chorus)

HE'S GOT THE WHOLE WORLD IN HIS HANDS 103

Traditional

C
1. He's got the whole world in His hands.
G^7
He's got the whole world in His hands.
C
He's got the whole world in His hands.
G^7 C
He's got the whole world in His hands.

2. He's got the wind and rain in His hands
He's got the wind and rain in His hands
He's got the wind and rain in His hands
He's got the whole world in His hands.

3. He's got you and me, brother, in His hands
He's got you and me, sister, in His hands
He's got you and me, brother, in His hands
He's got the whole world in His hands.

4. He's got the little bitty baby in His hands
He's got the little bitty baby in His hands
He's got the little bitty baby in His hands
He's got the whole world in His hands.

5. He's got everybody here in His hands
He's got everybody here in His hands
He's got everybody here in His hands
He's got the whole world in His hands.

104 GREAT IS THE LORD

Traditional

D A
Great is the Lord and greatly to be praised,

D
in the city of our God, in the mountain of His holiness.

D7 G
Beautiful for situation, the joy of the whole earth,

D
is Mt. Zion on the sides of the north,

A A7 D
the city of the great King.

Arrangement by Yohann Anderson 1970.

105 MICHAEL, ROW THE BOAT ASHORE

Traditional

Chorus:

C F C
Michael row the boat ashore al-le-lu-ia!

Em C G7 C
Michael row the boat ashore al-le-lu-ia!

C F C
1. Sister help to trim the sail – alleluia

Em F C G7 C
Sister help to trim the sail – alleluia.

(Chorus)

2. River Jordan is chilly and cold – alleluia.
Chills the body, not the soul – alleluia.

(Chorus)

3. The river is deep and the river is wide – alleluia
Milk and honey on the other side – alleluia.

(Chorus)

4. Brother lend a helping hand – alleluia
Brother lend a helping hand – alleluia.

(Chorus)

SWING LOW

Traditional

Chorus:

E A B^7 E B^7
Swing low, sweet chariot, Comin' for to carry me home,
E A B^7 E B^7 E A E
Swing low, sweet chariot, Comin' for to carry me home.

1. A B^7
I looked over Jordan and what did I see
E B^7
Comin' for to carry me home?
E A B^7
A band of angels comin' after me,
E B^7 E A E
Comin' for to carry me home.

(Chorus)

2. If you get there before I do -
Comin' for to carry me home,
Tell all my friends I'm comin' too
Comin' for to carry me home.

(Chorus)

3. I'm sometimes up and sometimes down,
Comin' for to carry me home,
But still my soul is glory bound.
Comin' for to carry me home.

(Chorus)

107 SHOWER THE PEOPLE YOU LOVE WITH LOVE

Words and Music by James Taylor

F C
1. You can play the game, you can act the part
Dm B♭
Though you know it wasn't written for you
F
But tell me how can you stand there
C C♯° Dm Csus4 C B♭
with your broken heart – ashamed of playing a fool
F C
One thing can lead to another
Dm B♭
it doesn't take any sacrifice
F C C♯°
Woh Father and Mother Sister and Brother
Dm C B♭ F/A
If it feels nice don't think twice
Gm7 C Csus4/D
Just shower the people you love with love
Gm7 C Dm C/D
Show them the way that you feel
Gm7 C C♯° Dm7 A 7
Think it's gonna work out fine if you only will
Gm7 C Dm C/D
Shower the people you love with love
Gm7 C C/D
Show them the way that you feel.
Gm7 C C♯° Dm E B
Things are gonna be much better, if you only will

2. You can run but you cannot hide
This is widely known
and what good is a man
with his foolish pride
when he's all by himself alone.
Once you tell somebody the way you feel
You can feel it beginning to ease
I think it's true what they say
about the squeaky wheel,
Always getting the grease.
I want you to shower the people you love with love
Show them the way that you feel
Think it's gonna work out fine if you only will
Shower the people you love with love
Show them the way that you feel
Things are gonna be much better, if you only will

```
          A°7
What I like to do to you is
  Gm7                                  C  C/D
shower the people you love with love.
  Gm7                              C Dm C/D
Show them the way that you feel.            (fade)
```

108 HE'S ALIVE

By Jerry Blacklaw

Chorus:

```
F  C Gm    C   F C Gm C
He – He  He's Alive      (repeat)
```

```
      F               Gm
1.    I can see above the clouds and
      Am              Bb                  C C7
      I can hear Him call my name out loud . . .
```

2. He has come that I might have life
And more life than I have had before . . .

109 ROCK MY SOUL

Traditional

```
        C
1.    Rock-a-my soul in the bosom of Abraham.
        G7
      Rock-a-my soul in the bosom of Abraham.
        C
      Rock-a-my soul in the bosom of Abraham.
      G7              C
      Oh, rock-a-my soul.

      C
2.    So high, can't get over it;
       G7
      So low can't get under it;
       C
      So wide, can't get around it;
      G7              C
      Oh, rock-a-my soul.

        C
3.    Rock, Rock, Rock my soul.
       G7
      Rock, Rock, Rock my soul.
        C
      Rock, Rock, Rock my soul.
      G7              C
      Oh, Rock my soul.
```

AMAZING GRACE

Traditional

Words by John Newton
Walker's Southern Harmony

1. Amazing grace, how sweet the sound (G G7 C G)
That saved a wretch like me! (Em D D7)
I once was lost, but now am found (G G7 C G)
Was blind, but now I see. (Em G D7 C G)

2. 'Twas grace that taught my heart to fear,
And grace my fears relieved;
How precious did that grace appear
The hour I first believed!

3. Through many dangers, toils, and snares,
I have already come;
'Tis grace has brought me safe thus far,
And grace will lead me home.

4. The Lord has promised good to me,
His word my hope secures;
He will my shield and portion be
As long as life endures.

5. And when this flesh and heart shall fail,
And mortal life shall cease;
I shall possess within the veil
A life of joy and peace.

6. When we've been there ten thousand years,
Bright shining as the sun,
We've no less days to sing God's praise
Than when we first begun.

111 HE'S EVERYTHING TO ME

Words and Music by Ralph Carmichael

G Em C D7
In the stars His handiwork I see,
G Em C D7
On the wind He speaks with majesty,
G G7 C Am7
Though He ruleth over land and sea,
G D7
What is that to me?
G Em C D7
I will celebrate Nativity,
G Em C D7
For it has a place in history,
G G7 C Am7
Sure, He came to set His people free,
G D7
What is that to me?

C
Chorus: Till by faith I met Him face to face,
Bm C
And I felt the wonder of His grace,
Then I knew that He was more
D7
than just a God who didn't care,
That lived a way out there and

G C D7
Now He walks beside me day by day,
G Em C D7
Ever watching o'er me lest I stray,
G C G
Helping me to find that narrow way,
D7 G
He's ev'rything to me.

(Chorus)

I SAW A MAN

Words and Music by Orien Johnson

Am Dm E7 Am
1. I saw a Man hanging on a tree,
Dm E
I saw a Man hanging on a tree;
Dm Am
A lonely tree on Calvary,
Dm E7 Am
I saw a Man hanging on a tree.

2. I watched His heart break in agony,
I watched His heart break in agony,
I saw Him die against the sky.
I watched His heart break in agony.

3. I saw His love flowing out to me,
I saw His love flowing out to me,
And, as He died against the sky
I saw His love flowing out to me.

4. Come, walk with me, Brothers of the Way
Come, walk with me, Brothers of the Way
As day by day He leads the way,
Come, walk with me, Brothers of the Way.

5. O come with me to the world He loved
O come with me to the world He loved
Our life to give that men may live
O come with me to the world He loved.

113 FOR WHAT IT'S WORTH

Words and Music by Stephen Stills

Slow rock beat

```
  E                                 A
There's something happening here,
    E                        A
What it is ain't exactly clear,
           E                      A
There's a man with a gun over there,
       E               A
Tellin' me I've got to beware.
```

Chorus:

```
                                     E
I think it's time we stop, children, what's that sound?
  A                            E A E A
Everybody look what's goin' down.
```

```
              E                   A
1.      There's battle lines bein' drawn,
                        E                      A
        Nobody's right if everybody's wrong.
          E                               A
        Young people speakin' their minds,
                  E                        A
        Gettin' so much resistance from behind.
```

(Chorus)

2. What a field day for the heat.
A thousand people in the street
Singin' songs and carryin' signs.
Mostly saying, "Hooray for our side."

(Chorus)

3. Paranoia strikes deep,
Into your life it will creep.
It starts when you're always afraid.
Step out of line the men come and
take you away.

You better stop, hey, what's that sound? Everybody
look what's going down.
(repeat and fade out)

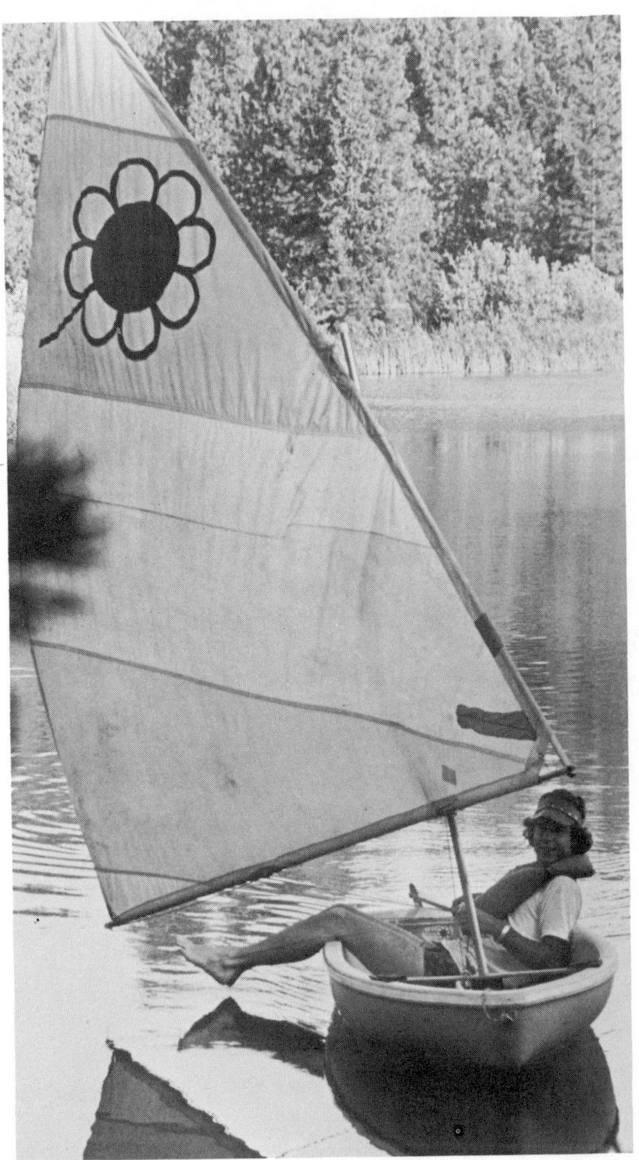

114 BATTLE HYMN OF THE REPUBLIC

Words by Julia Ward Howe
Music by William Steffe, arr.

(Guitar Key G)

G
1. Mine eyes have seen the glory

of the coming of the Lord;
C
He is trampling out the vintage
G D^7
where the grapes of wrath are stored;
G
He hath loosed the fateful lightning
E^m
of His terrible swift sword:
C D^7 G
His truth is marching on.

Chorus:
G
Glory! glory! Hallelujah!
C G D^7
Glory! glory! Hallelujah!
G E^m C D^7 G
Glory! glory! Hallelujah! His truth is marching on.

2. I have seen Him in the watchfires
of a hundred circling camps;
They have builded Him an altar
in the evening dews and damps;
I can read His righteous sentence
by the dim and flaring lamps:
His day is marching on.

(Chorus)

3. He has sounded forth the trumpet
that shall never call retreat;
He is sifting out the hearts
of men before His judgment seat;
O be swift, my soul, to answer Him!
Be jubilant, my feet!
Our God is marching on.

(Chorus)

4. In the beauty of the lilies
Christ was born across the sea,
With a glory in His bosom
that transfigures you and me:
As He died to make men holy,
Let us die to make men free,
While God is marching on.

(Chorus)

BEHOLD WHAT MANNER OF LOVE 115

Words and Music by Patricia Van Tine

```
    C                   F                   C         G
Behold what manner of love the Father has given unto us.
    C                   F                   C        G C
Behold what manner of love the Father has given unto us.
    C   F             C               G
* That we should be called the sons of God.
    C   F             C          G    C
  That we should be called the sons of God.
```

* *round begins here.*

Verse 2:

Love Him, trust Him, give Him glory
Love Him, trust Him, give Him praise, Alleluia, Alleluia

116 ALL HAIL THE POWER

Words by Edward Perronet (1726-1792)
stanza 4 John Rippon (1751-1836)

Music by James Ellor (1819-1899)

```
           A                      D  E    A
1.    All hail the pow'r of Jesus' name!
          A       D        A
      Let angels prostrate fall.
          D      A/E    E  A
      Let angels prostrate fall:
                         C#m     E    A
      Bring forth the royal diadem,
```

Chorus:

```
                        D                            A
Women:  And crown  Men: (crown Him, crown Him,
                                        E            A
                            crown Him,) Him,
                                       D             E
Men:      Crown  Women:  (crown Him, crown Him,
                                       A
                           crown Him,) Him,
                           D     A/E  E7  A
Unison:  And crown Him Lord of all.
```

2. Ye chosen seed of Israel's race:
Ye ransomed from the fall.
Ye ransomed from the fall:
Hail Him who saves you by His grace,

(Chorus)

3. Sinners, whose love can ne'er forget
The wormwood and the gall.
The wormwood and the gall:
Go, spread your trophies at His feet,

(Chorus)

4. Let ev'ry kindred, ev'ry tribe,
On this terrestrial ball.
On this terrestrial ball:
To Him all majesty ascribe,

(Chorus)

5. O that with yonder sacred throng
We at His feet may fall.
We at His feet may fall!
We'll join the everlasting song,

(Chorus)

117 THEY HUNG HIM ON A CROSS

Traditional

1.
      D
They hung him on a cross
      D
They hung him on a cross
      D   A
They hung him on a cross for me,
      D D^7
One day when I was lost (so lost)
      G G^7
They hung him on a cross (oh yeah)
      D   A   D
They hung him on a cross for me.

2. They whipped him up a hill
They whipped him up a hill
They whipped him up a hill for me,
One day when I was lost (so lost)
They whipped him up a hill (oh yeah)
They whipped him up a hill for me.

3. They speared him in the side
They speared him in the side
They speared him in the side for me,
One day when I was lost (so lost)
They speared him in the side (oh yeah)
They speared him in the side for me.

4. Then, he hung his head and he died
Then, he hung his head and he died
Then, he hung his head and he died for me,
One day when I was lost (so lost)
Then, he hung his head and he died (oh yeah)
Then, he hung his head and he died for me.

5. Triumphant was his cry
Triumphant was his cry
Triumphant was his cry for me,
One day when I was lost (so lost)
Triumphant was his cry (oh yeah)
Triumphant was his cry for me.

6. They laid him in a tomb
They laid him in a tomb
They laid him in a tomb for me,
One day when I was lost (so lost)
They laid him in the tomb (oh yeah)
They laid him in the tomb for me.

7. He rose on Easter morn
He rose on Easter morn
He rose on Easter morn for me,
One day when I was lost (so lost)
He rose on Easter morn (oh yeah)
He rose on Easter morn for me.

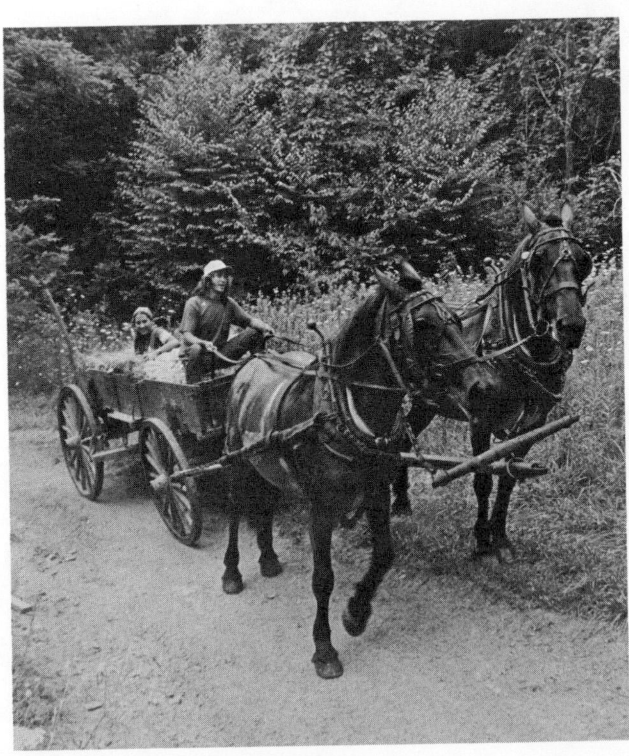

118 MAN OF SORROWS

Traditional

Philip Bliss (1838-1976)

C A^m E
1. "Man of Sorrows," what a name
F C D^7 G
For the Son of God who came
C C
Ruined sinners to reclaim!
G A^m F C
Hallelujah! what a Savior!

2. Bearing shame and scoffing rude,
In my place condemned He stood,
Sealed my pardon with His blood:
Hallelujah! what a Savior!

3. Guilty vile and helpless, we:
Spotless Lamb of God was He:
"Full atonement!" can it be?
Hallelujah! what a Savior!

4. "Lifted up" was He to die,
"It is finished," was His cry:
Now in heav'n exalted high:
Hallelujah! what a Savior!

5. When He comes, our glorious King,
All His ransomed home to bring.
Then anew this song we'll sing:
Hallelujah! what a Savior!

WHEN THE SPIRIT SAYS MOVE 119

Traditional

A^{m} D A^{m}
When the Spirit says move you've got to *move* (uh, uh).
C E
When the Spirit says move you gotta *move* (uh, uh).
A^{m} D
When the Spirit says move you gotta *move,* Oh Lord
A^{m} E A^{m}
When the Spirit says move you gotta *move*

(uh), *move* (uh) *move* (uh, uh).

2.	**Shout**	**7.**	**Talk-mumble**
3.	**Sing**	**8.**	**Laugh**
4.	**Clap**	**9.**	**(make up own)**
5.	**Listen**	**10.**	**End with stop**
6.	**Hic-up**		

THINKIN' 120

Unknown

C(G) F(C) B♭(F) E(C)
1. Thinkin' about
F(C) F(C) B♭(F) C(F)
Thinkin', Thinkin', Thinkin', Thinkin', (repeat)
C(G)
Thinkin' about *thinkin'* in a song.
F^{7}(C^{7}) F(C) G(D)
Tell it to the people as you pass along
C(G) G(D) C(G) F(C) C(G) F^{m}(B^{m}) A^{m}(F^{m})
Singin' glory, glory, glory ha- le- lu- ia
F(C) G(D) C(G^{7})
Praise the Lord in a song
F(C) C(G) F(C) C(G)
do do-in oo wah do do-in do whah
F(C) C(G)
do do-in do wah.

2. *Freedom*
3. *Love*
4. *Life*

121 I'LL FLY AWAY

Words and Music by Albert E. Brumley

```
          G
1.   Some glad morning when this life is o'er,
      C      G
     I'll fly away,
      G
     To a home on God's celestial shore,
         D7   G C G
     I'll fly away.

         G D G              G7    C    G   C G
Chorus: I'll fly away, O glory, I'll fly away;
             C    G                            G/D D7   G  C G
        When I die, hallelujah, by and by — I'll fly away.
```

2. When the shadows of this life have grown,
I'll fly away,
Like a bird from prison bars has flown,
I'll fly away.

3. Just a few more weary days, and then
I'll fly away,
To a land where joys shall never end,
I'll fly away.

122 WIDE DEEP LONG AND HIGH

Ephesians 3:18—19

By Jerry Blacklaw

```
                            E
(A two-part round!)   How wide and deep and long and high
                            B7
                      How wide and deep and long and high
                            E
                      How wide and deep and long and high
                            B7     E
                      is the love of God
                            E     G      A    E
                      How Wide Deep Long High (repeat)

                      (Repeat)
```

THE WORD

By Jerry Blacklaw

Chorus:

```
 A7                          D
Yes He spoke through the Word.
 Gbm                               Bm
Through the Word he has been heard.
  G                      D                       A7
He's abiding with us still if we seek to do His will,
                               D
Having spoken through the Word.
 A7                         D
And the Word became a man,
 Gbm                         Bm
and He dwelled upon this land.
 G                           D                           A7
And He shows what God is like, turns existence into life.
                               D
Having spoken through the Word.
```

```
       D       C           G                 D
1.     One day we will understand the world we live in
       C               G                   Bm
       We will understand what we've been given.
        E      A     G    D
       One day it will all be plain.
```

2. Creation, God's own personal expression
Came into His own creation
We see Him, full of grace and truth.

3. In Him was life, the light of all mankind
Shining in the darkness of doubt
And the darkness, has never put it out.

124 TAKE IT EASY

Words and Music by Jackson, Browne and Glen Frye

Guitar Capo 2 — Key D
Moderate Country Style

1. D
Well, I'm a runnin' down the road

try'n to loosen my load,

A G
I've got seven women on my mind,

D A
four that wanna own me, two that wanna stone me,

G D
one says she's a friend of mine.

Bm G D
Take it easy, take it easy,

Em G
don't let the sound of your own wheels

Bm
drive you crazy.

G D
Lighten up while you still can,

G D
don't even try to understand,

Em G D
just find a place to make your stand and take it easy.

2. Well, I'm a standin' on a corner
in Winslow, Arizona,
and such a fine sight to see
It's a girl, my Lord, in a flat-bed Ford
slowin' down to take a look at me.
Come on, baby, don't say maybe,
I gotta know if your sweet love is gonna save me.
We may lose and we may win,
though we will never be here again,
So open up, I'm climbin' in, so take it easy.

3. **Well, I'm a runnin' down the road**
try'n to loosen my load,
got a world of trouble on my mind,
Lookin' for a lover who won't blow my cover,
she's so hard to find.
Take it easy, take it easy.
Don't let the sound of your own wheels
make you crazy.
Come on baby, don't say maybe
I gotta know if your sweet love is gonna save me.

DAY BY DAY — 125

By Stephen Schwartz

Fmj7 Gm7 Fmj7 Gm7 (B♭)
Day by day, Day by day
Am7 Cmj7(Em) G6(G)
Oh, dear Lord, three things I pray.
Em A7 Em A7 Dm
To see Thee more clearly, love Thee more dearly,
G7(Em)
Follow Thee more nearly
Cmj7 Fmj7(Em) Fmj7
day by day, day by day.

(repeat as many times as you want. End with G.)

126 COME TO THE WATER
(For Those Tears I Died)

Chorus:
E7 A E
And Jesus said, "Come to the water, stand by my side.
B7 E E7
I know you are thirsty, you won't be denied.
A E
I felt every teardrop when in darkness you cried.
B7 B7 E
And I long to remind you that for those tears I died."

E C♯m A B7
1. You said you'd come and share all my sorrows.
E C♯m A B7
You said you'd be there for all my tomorrows.
E B A B
I came so close to sending you away.
E C♯m A B
But just like you promised, You came in to stay.
B7 E E7
I just had to pray.

(Chorus)

2. Your goodness is so great I can't understand.
But, dear Lord, I know now that all this was planned.
I know you are here now and always will be.
Your love burst my chains and in you I'm free.
But, Jesus, why me?

(Chorus)

3. Jesus, I give you my heart and my soul.
I know that without you I'll never be whole.
Saviour, you opened all the right doors.
And I thank you and praise you from
Earth's humble shores.
Take me, I'm yours.

(Chorus)

SOMEBODY TOUCHED ME 127

Traditional American spiritual

NOTE: Try singing "Do Lord" or "This Little Light of Mine" or "Worried Man Blues" or "We're Gonna Sit at the Welcome Table" with this song. They all have the same root tune and chord progression.

G G^7
1. **While I was singing somebody touched me;**
C C^7 G
While I was singing somebody touched me;
G B^7 E^m
While I was singing somebody touched me;
A^7 D^7 G C G D^7
It must have been the hand of the Lord!

Chorus:

G G G^7
Glory, glory, glory! Somebody touched me.
C C^7 G
Glory, glory, glory! Somebody touched me.
G B^7 E^m
Glory, glory, glory! Somebody touched me;
A^7 D^7 G C G
It must have been the hand of the Lord!

2. **While I was praying somebody touched me;**
While I was praying somebody touched me;
While I was praying somebody touched me;
It must have been the hand of the Lord!

(Chorus)

3. **While I was preaching somebody touched me;**
While I was preaching somebody touched me;
While I was preaching somebody touched me;
It must have been the hand of the Lord!

(Chorus)

128 LOOK ALL AROUND YOU

By John Fischer

Chorus:

D Em G D
Look all around you and see what is real;
D Em A7 D
Hear what is true and be sure what you feel.
D Em G D
Touch someone near you in love if you can,
D Em A7 D
Give all you have and be part of God's plan.

1. C D
Life is always shallow
C D
When you fail to see,
C Bm
That living for yourself
E7 A (B♭ D)
Will never make you free.

(Chorus)

2. You may live a lifetime
Doomed to hate and fear,
Because you could not see
Beyond your selfish tears.

(Chorus)

3. Life can be so meaningful
When you finally see
That only in His love
Will you be really free.

(Chorus)

REACH OUT AND TOUCH
(Somebody's Hand)

Words and Music by Nickolas Ashford and Valerie Simpson

Chorus:

A^{m7} G^7 C^{maj7}
Reach out and touch somebody's hand,
A^{m7} D^{m7} G^7 C A^{m7}
Make this world a better place if you can. (just try)
A^{m7} G^7 C^{maj7}
Reach out and touch somebody's hand,
A^{m7} D^{m7} G^7 E^{m7}
Make this world a better place if you can.

C^{maj7} F
1. Take a little time out of your busy day,
F^+ F^6 D^{m7}
To give encouragement to someone
E^m E^{m7} A^{m7}
who's lost the way. (just try)
C^{maj7} F F^+ F^6
Or would I be talking to a stone if I asked you
D^{m7} G^{m7} A^7
to share a problem that's not your own
C^7 F A^m D^{m7}
We can change things if we start giving.
G^9
Why don't you

(Chorus)

2. If you see an old friend on the street,
and he's down, remember,
his shoes could fit your feet.
Just try a little kindness and you'll see it's something
that comes very naturally.
We can change things if we start giving.
Why don't you (why don't you)
reach out and touch somebody's hand.

130 HAVE YOU SEEN JESUS MY LORD

By John Fischer

(intro: C F Em Dm7)

```
                  C      E          F   Ab
Chorus:  Have you seen Jesus my Lord?
           C   G7             C (F Em Dm7)
         He's here in plain view.
                  C      E        F   Ab
         Take a look, open your eyes,
          C      G7   Em(open) C
         He'll show it to you.

                   Am                    Em
   1.     Have you ever looked at the sunset
                   F G          C
          With the sky mellowin' red,
                   Am                     Em
          And the clouds suspended like feathers?
                   F            C    G7  Em7   C
          Then I say you've seen Jesus my Lord.
```

2. Have you ever stood at the ocean
With the white foam at your feet,
Felt the endless thunderin' motion?
Then I say you've seen Jesus my Lord.

3. Have you ever looked at the cross,
With a man hangin' in pain
And the look of love in His eyes?
Then I say you've seen Jesus my Lord.

4. Have you ever stood in the family
With the Lord there in your midst,
Seen the face of Christ on your brother?
Then I say you've seen Jesus my Lord.

HOW FIRM A FOUNDATION, YE SAINTS OF THE LORD 131

Traditional American Melody

Capo 2

D^7 G C G D G D D^7
1. How firm a foundation, ye saints of the Lord,
G C G E^m G D D^7 G
Is laid for your faith in His excellent word!
G E^m C G D
What more can He say than to you He hath said,
D^7 G C G C G D D^7 G
To you who for refuge to Jesus have fled.

2. "Fear not, I am with thee, O be not dismayed,
For I am thy God, and will still give thee aid;
I'll strengthen thee, help thee, and cause thee to stand
Upheld by My righteous, omnipotent hand.

3. "When through the deep waters I call thee to go,
The rivers of sorrow shall not overflow;
For I will be with thee, thy troubles to bless,
And sanctify to thee thy deepest distress.

4. "When through fiery trials thy pathway shall lie,
My grace, all sufficient, shall be thy supply;
The flame shall not hurt thee; I only design
Thy dross to consume, and thy gold to refine.

5. "The soul that on Jesus hath leaned for repose,
I will not, I will not desert to his foes;
That soul, though all hell should endeavor to shake,
I'll never, no never, no never forsake!"

132 WALKIN' IN THE LIGHT

By Jerry Blacklaw

Chorus:

Guys: (sing two lines three times)

A B^{m7}
Walkin', Walkin' Walkin' in the Light
A B^{m7}
Walkin', Walkin' Walkin' in the Light

Gals: (Start after guys sing once)

A B^{m7} A B^{m7}
Walkin' in the light — oo — we can trust each other
A B^{m7} A
Walkin' in the light — we can see ourselves.

B^{m7} A B^{m7}
1. It's a sad situation
A B^{m7}
People running scared
A
It's a crazy mixed up world
D E^7 A
Where there's nothing to fear but fear

(Chorus)

2. We always walk in darkness
Forget about the day —
We're afraid to face our problems
We're hoping they'll go away.

(Chorus)

3. So we finally pull our heads
Out of the sand
There is light and warmth of sunshine
And it never is dark again.

(Chorus)

IT'S JUST YOU 133

Words and Music by Jerry Blacklaw

```
     Cmaj7                                Dmaj7
1.   It's just you who makes me wonder
     Cmaj7                                Dmaj7       D
     It's just you who makes me wonder, wonder
      Am                    D
     How can I know you
      Am                D
     How can I be free
       G                   F                C                   D
     How can I know you when I really don't know me?
```

2. It's just you who makes me question
It's just you who makes me question, question
How can I know you
How can I be free
How can I know you when I really don't know me.

3. It's just you who makes me satisified
It's just you who makes me satisfied, satisfied
Is this part of life, learning what to do
I'll know more of me as I'm learning more of you . . .

134 SWEET, SWEET SONG OF SALVATION

Words and Music by Larry Norman

Chorus:

G
Sing that sweet, sweet song of salvation,
D^7
and let your laughter fill the air;
D^7
Sing that sweet, sweet song of salvation,
C^7 G
and tell the people everywhere.
G^7
Sing that sweet, sweet song of salvation
C A^7
to ev'ry man and every nation;
G C
Sing that sweet, sweet song of salvation,
G D^7 C C^7 G
and let the people know that Jesus cares.

G

1. When you know a pretty story,

D

you don't let it go unsaid.

You tell it to your children

C G

as you tuck them into bed.

G^7

And when you know a wonderful secret

C A^7

you tell it to your friends,

G G^7 C

because a lifetime filled with happiness

G D^7 G

is like a street that never ends.

(Chorus)

2. Look around you as you sing it
There are people everywhere
And to those who stop and listen
This sweet song becomes a prayer
'Cause when you know a wonderful secret
You tell it to your friends
Tell them that a lifetime filled with Jesus
Is like a street that never ends.

(Chorus)

135 LET MY LIGHT SHINE BRIGHT

Words and Music by Sam Vofkerichian

Chorus:

            G   D
Let my light shine bright,
                   C   G
through the night, through the day,
          D   G C G
All the way for you. (twice)

          G   D
1. **When I fall you come around**
                 C   G
You pick me up from off the ground.
                 G   D
When I'm down you're always there
            C   G C G
To lift me up because you care.

(Chorus)

2. **People try, try to be free**
But they're not, why can't they see
That you died to set me free
For all eternity?

(Chorus)

3. **I try to live life on my own**
Doing the good things that you have shown
But I can't without you Lord,
Without your help, without your word.

(Chorus)

STANDIN' IN THE NEED OF PRAYER 136

Traditional

Chorus:

E
It's me, it's me, it's me, O Lord,
B^7 E
Standin' in the need of prayer.

It's me, it's me, it's me, O Lord,
B^7 E
Standin' in the need of prayer.

E
1. Not my mother, nor my father, but it's me, O Lord,
B^7 E
Standin' in the need of prayer.

Not my sister nor my brother but it's me, O Lord,
B^7 E
Standin' in the need of prayer.

(Chorus)

2. Not the deacon, not the preacher, but it's me, O Lord,
Standin' in the need of prayer.
Not the elder, not the teacher, but it's me, O Lord,
Standin' in the need of prayer.

(Chorus)

137 ALL MY TRIALS

Traditional

Chorus:

```
    C
It's late my brothers
                       F  Fm
It's late, but never mind
C Em  Am       Dm    G G7 G       C
All – all my trials Lord, soon be over.
```

```
     C                                        B♭ (F=6th Fret)
1.  If livin' was a thing that money could buy
        C           Em                           F  Fm
    The rich would live and the poor would die
    C Em  Am       Dm    G   G7   G  C
    All – all my trials Lord, soon be over.
```

2. I had a little book, it was given to me
And each new page spelled liberty
All – all my trials Lord, soon be over.

(Chorus)

3. Think you people, don't you cry
My Lord condemned not, nor do I.
All – all my trials Lord, soon be over.

4. See the land across the sea,
And the people crying, come set us free.
All – all my trials Lord, soon be over.

(Chorus)

AWAKE OH ISRAEL 138

Traditional

Awake Oh Israel, put off thy slumber
For the truth shall set you free
From out of Zion comes thy deliverer
In the year of jubilee.

Thou art my chosen, for I have sought thee
Thou art graven on my hand
And I will gather all those who scatter
And return them to their land.

Out of the furnace of much affliction
I have chosen thee behold
And for iron I'll give thee silver
And for brass I'll give thee gold.

Oh Allelujah, Oh Allelujah
Allelujah – Praise the Lord!
(Repeat)

139

BY MY SIDE

From the Musical production GODSPELL

Words by Jay Hamburger
Music by Peggy Gordon

Dmin C C/B Amin
Where are you going? Where are you going?
Dmin C C/B
Will you take me with you?
Amin Dmin C C/B
For my hand is cold and needs warmth . . .
Amin Dmin D
Where are you going?
C D
Far beyond where the horizon lies
C
where the horizon lies,
D C
and the land sinks into mellow blueness, oh, please,
D
take me with you . . .
C D
Let me skip the road with you,
C D
I can dare myself, I can dare myself . . .
C D C
I'll put a pebble in my shoe and watch me walk
D
I can walk and walk . . .
Dmin C C/B Amin
I shall call the pebble dare –
Dmin C C/B
We will talk together, about walking . . .
Amin Dmin C C/B
Dare shall be carried, and when we both have had enough,
Amin Dmin
I will take him from my shoe, singing
C C/B Amin
"Meet your new road . . ."

Dmin C C/B
Then I'll take your hand — finally glad
Amin Dmin C C/B Amin
That you are here by my side (by my side)
Dmin C C/B Amin
By my side (by my side)
Dmin C C/B Amin
By my side (that you are here by my side).

GO WHERE I SEND THEE 140

Traditional

C
Children, go where — I send thee,

How shall I send thee?

Well, I'm gonna send you

One by one, One for the little bitty

F C G C
baby — was born, born, born in Bethlehem.

Send you two by two, for Paul and Silas
Send you three by three, three for the Hebrew children
Send you four by four, four for the four that stood
at the door.
Send you five by five, five for the Gospel Preachers.
Send you six by six, six for the six that never got fixed
Send you seven by seven, seven for the seven that try to get
to heaven.
Send you eight by eight, eight for the eight that stood at
the gate.

141 DOWN BY THE RIVERSIDE

Traditional

1\. D
I'm gonna lay down my sword and shield,
A
Down by the riverside, down by the riverside,
D
down by the riverside.

I'm gonna lay down my sword and shield,
A^7 D
Down by the riverside, down by the riverside.

Chorus:

G
Well, I ain't gonna study war no more,
D
I ain't gonna study war no more,
A D
I ain't gonna study war no more. (repeat chorus)

2\. I'm gonna walk with the Prince of Peace,
Down by the riverside, down by the riverside,
down by the riverside.
I'm gonna walk with the Prince of Peace,
Down by the riverside, down by the riverside.

(Chorus)

3\. Yes, I'm gonna shake hands around the world,
Down by the riverside, down by the riverside,
down by the riverside.
Yes, I'm gonna shake hands around the world,
Down by the riverside, down by the riverside.

(Chorus)

HALLELU, HALLELU 142

Key: E or when using music book play in F or capo up 1 while playing in E.

E A
Hallelu, hallelu, hallelu, hallelujah;
E B7 E
Praise ye the Lord!
E A
Hallelu, hallelu, hallelu, hallelujah;
E B7 E
Praise ye the Lord!
E B7
Praise ye the Lord! Hallelujah;
E
Praise ye the Lord, Hallelujah;
A
Praise ye the Lord, Hallelujah;
B7 E
Praise ye the Lord.

143 CHRIST AROSE

Public Domain

By Robert Lowry

Chorus:

. . . . . . He arose Alleluia Christ arose
May the book of life never close
Til the whole world knows, the whole world knows
He arose.

1. History began long ago many years before man
There's so much that we don't know
that went into God's plan.
Why do stars stay awake in the heavens
Why do atoms behave as they do
For what God has revealed, no man can conceal
It's a message pure and good.

(Because He arose . . . .) (Chorus)

2. Evil prevailed in the world so long what was God to do
Then a man named Jesus came along
and spoke of the good and true.
For his love they repaid him with hatred,
For compassion, he hung on the cross
When it looked like the end, did the
hope God did send
lie at last in a tragic loss.

(Oh, No, He arose . . . .) (Chorus)

3. No one knows when he's coming again
like he said he would
He's just giving us time to help mankind
receive him as they should.
When he comes in a beautiful splendor
And calls all his own to his side
I'm so glad I'll be there, there's no need to despair,
When in Him we do abide.

(Because He arose . . . .) (Chorus)

JESUS IS THE ROCK 'N' HE ROLLS MY BLUES AWAY

Chorus:

Jesus is the Rock 'n' He rolls my blues away
Jesus is the Rock 'n' He rolls my blues away
Jesus is the Rock 'n' He rolls my blues away

1. When you're out on the street
And you really feel down and lo
When you're out on the street
And there's no place to go
When you're out on the street,
Well, Jesus gonna save your soul, cause . . .

(Chorus)

2. When you wake up in the mornin
And the sky ain't bright 'n' blue
When you wake up in the mornin
And the big world's after you
When you wake up in the mornin
Jesus gonna pull you thru, cause . . .

(Chorus)

3. When you look in the mirror
and your face causes it to crack
When you're thru with your day
and you feel like you've been attacked
Well, Jesus gonna love you
and Baby, now that's a fact, cause . . .

(Chorus)

145 JUST A CLOSER WALK WITH THEE

Traditional Spiritual

Chorus:

G D^7 G
Just a closer walk with Thee – Grant it Jesus, if you please;
G^7 C G D^7 G
Daily walking close to Thee – Let it be, dear Lord, let it be.

G D^7
1. I am weak but Thou art strong –
G
Jesus, keep me from all wrong;
G^7 C
I'll be satisfied as long –
G D^7 G
As I walk, dear Lord, close to Thee.

(Chorus)

2. Thru this world of toil and snares,
If I falter, Lord, who cares?
Who with me my burden shares?
None but Thee, dear Lord, none but Thee.

(Chorus)

3. When my feeble life is o'er,
Time for me will be no more;
On that bright eternal shore
I will walk, dear Lord, close to Thee.

(Chorus)

KING JESUS — 146

Unknown

(sung as an echo: King Jesus is all – King Jesus is all)

King Jesus is all,
My all and all.
I know He'll answer
me when I call.
Walkin' by my side,
I'm satisfied,
King Jesus is all,
my all and all.

(unison) **Well, I went out to meet the Lord (oh yeah!)**
I got down on my knees.
I prayed my last prayer.
You know the Holy Ghost met me there.
I stepped on a rock.
The rock was sound (oo-oo).
The love of God came a tumblin' down.
The reason I know that he saved my soul,
'is' I dug down deep and I found pure gold.
an' he's all – (chorus)

KUM BA YAH — 147

(Come By Here)

Traditional

```
  C                     F       C
Kum ba yah, my Lord, Kum ba yah.
           Em           F        G
Kum ba yah, my Lord, Kum ba yah.
           C            F       C
Kum ba yah, my Lord, Kum ba yah.
 F    C     G     C
Oh, Lord, Kum ba yah.
```

Someone's singing, Lord, Kum ba yah.
Someone's crying, Lord, Kum ba yah.
Someone's praying, Lord, Kum ba yah.
Come by here, my Lord, come by here.
(Add own verses – sing freely)

148 RICH MAN SPIRITUAL

Words and Music by Gordon Lightfoot

C Em
1. I'm gonna buy me a long white robe
F G
Yes, Lord, to help me home
C Em
I'm gonna buy me a long white robe
F G
Yes, Lord, to get me home
C C7
And when I get my heavenly gown
F Ab
And I lay my burden down
C A D
I'm gonna get me a long white robe
G C G C
To get me home.

2. I'm gonna buy me two golden slippers
Yes, Lord, to walk me home
I'm gonna buy me two golden slippers
Yes, Lord, to walk me home
And when I get my slippers of gold
Then Lord will have my soul
I'm gonna get me two golden slippers
To walk me home.

3. I'm gonna buy me two wings of silver
Yes, Lord, to fly me home
I'm gonna buy me two wings of silver
Yes, Lord, to fly me home
And when I get my silvery wings
And an angel choir will sing
I'm gonna get me two wings of silver
To get me home.

4. I'm gonna buy me a poor man's troubles
Yes, Lord, to help me home
I'm gonna buy me a poor man's troubles
Yes, Lord, to help me home
And when I get my troublin' woes
Then homeward I will go
I'm gonna get a little troublin' woes
To get me home.

5. I'm gonna find me a smilin' angel
Yes, Lord, to lead me home
I'm gonna get me a smilin' angel
Yes, Lord, to lead me home
And when she takes me by the hand
Then Lord we'll understand
(Slower) I'm gonna get me a smilin' angel
To lead me home.

149 YOU AIN'T GOIN' NOWHERE

Words and Music by Bob Dylan

(G, A^m C)

Chorus:

Ooo Eee ride me high
Tomorrow's the day my bride's gonna come
Oh Lord we're gonna fly
Down in my easy chair.

1. Clouds so swift the rain won't lift
Gate won't close the railin's froze
Get your mind off 'a winter time
Cause you ain't goin' nowhere.

2. Ghengis Khan and his brother Don
Could not keep on keepin' on
We'll climb that mountain no matter how steep
When we feel up to it.

3. Ghengis Khan he could not keep
All his shieks supplied with sleep
Cross that mountain no matter how steep
'Cause you ain't goin' nowhere.

4. I don't care how many letters you sent
Morning came and mornin' went
Pick up your money and pack up your tent
'Cause you ain't goin' nowhere

5. Buy me a flute and a gun that shoots
Tailgates and substitutes
Strap yourself to a tree with roots
'Cause you ain't goin' nowhere.

TAKE ME HOME, COUNTRY ROADS 150

Words and Music by Bill Danoff, Taffy Danoff and John Denver

```
                A    F♯m
1.   Almost heaven, West Virginia,
       E                          D         A
     Blue Ridge Mountains, Shenandoah River.
                       F♯m
     Life is old there, older than the trees.
         E                         D           A
     Younger than the mountains growin' like a breeze.
```

Chorus:

```
         A                E             F♯m         D
Country Roads, take me home to the place I belong:
       A                  E
West Virginia, mountain momma,
          D              A
Take me home, Country Roads.
```

2. All my memories gather 'round her,
miner's lady, stranger to blue water.
Dark and dusty, painted on the sky,
misty taste of moonshine, teardrop in my eye.

(Chorus)

```
F♯m            E              A
I hear her voice, in the mornin' hour she calls me,
        D      A                  E
the radio reminds me of my home far away,
    F♯m                  G          D
And drivin' down the road I get a feelin'
        A                      E            E7
that I should have been home yesterday, yesterday.
```

(Chorus)

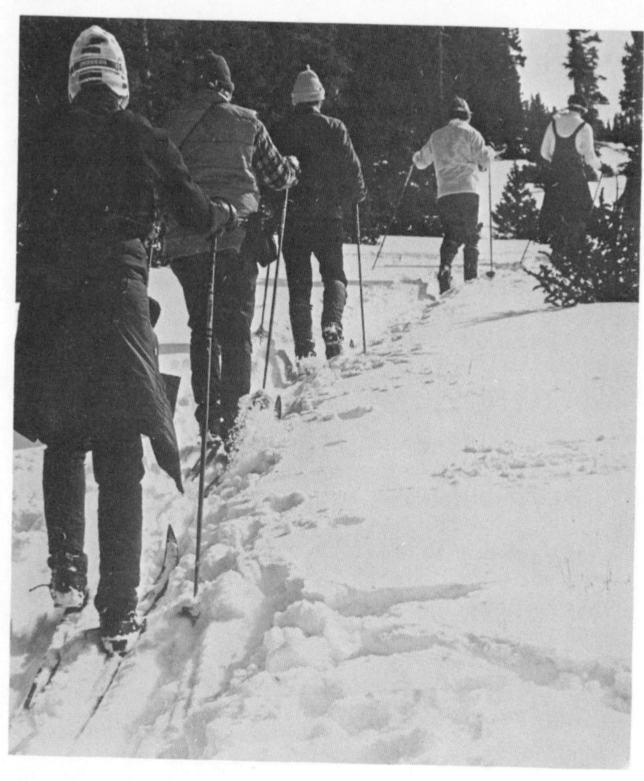

151 SPIRIT OF THE LIVING GOD

Spirit of the living God
Fall afresh on me.
Spirit of the living God
Fall afresh on me.
Melt me, mold me, fill me, use me,
Spirit of the living God
Fall afresh on me.

CAUSE ME TO KNOW THY LOVING KINDNESS 152

Cause me to know thy loving kindness in the morning,
for in thee do I trust,
Cause me to know the way wherein I should walk,
for I lift up my soul unto thee.
Deliver me, O Lord, teach me to do thy will,
Quicken me, O Lord,
for I stretch forth my hands unto thee.

Psalm 143

153 AIN'T GOT TIME TO DIE

Words and Music by Hall Johnson

1. Lord, I keep so busy prasin' my Jesus,
Keep so busy praisin' my Jesus,
Keep so busy praisin' my Jesus,
Ain't got time to die.

'Cause when I'm healin' de sick I'm praisin' my Jesus
When I'm healin' de sick I'm praisin' my Jesus
When I'm healin' de sick I'm praisin' my Jesus
Ain't got time to die.

'Cause it takes all o' ma time to praise my Jesus.
Takes all o' ma time to praise my Jesus.
If I don' praise Him de rocks gonter cry out,
"Glory an' honor, glory an' honor!"
Ain't got time to die.

2. Lord, I keep so busy workin' for de kingdom,
Keep so busy workin' for de kingdom,
Keep so busy workin' for de kingdom,
Ain't got time to die.

'Cause when I'm feedin' de po'
I'm workin' for de kingdom
When I'm feedin' de po'
I'm workin' for de kingdom
When I'm feedin' de po'
I'm workin' for de kingdom
Ain't got time to die.

'Cause it takes all o' ma time to praise my Jesus.
Takes all o' ma time to praise my Jesus.
If I don' praise Him de rocks gonter cry out,
"Glory an' honor, glory an' honor!"
Ain't got time to die.

3. Lord, I keep so busy servin' my Master,
Keep so busy servin' my Master,
Keep so busy servin' my Master,
Ain't got time to die.

'Cause when I'm giving my all I'm servin' my Master
When I'm giving my all I'm servin' my Master
When I'm giving my all I'm servin' my Master
Ain't got time to die.

Now won't you git out o' ma way
lemme praise my Jesus?
Now won't you git out o' ma way
lemme praise my Lord?
If I don' praise Him de rocks gonter cry out,
"Glory an' honor, glory an' honor!"
Ain't got time to die.

154 CERT'NLY, LORD

Spiritual

By Charles Cooke and Harry Robert Wilson

(Traditionally spirituals such as "Certainly Lord" and "Ain't Got Time to Die" are sung by a solo voice asking a question or starting the statement – and then answered by the group. The tempo is bright with syncopation, but not hurried.)

Gotta be ready when the good Lord comes,
Yes! Sisters, Brothers too.
Gotta be sure to keep the Golden Rule.
Yes! Sisters, Brothers too.

Get ready, time is nigh, to meet Him bye and bye,
When He calls, time to shout, Just sing right out!

Have you got good religion? Cert'nly Lord!
Have you got good religion? Cert'nly Lord!
Have you got good religion? Cert'nly Lord!
Cert'nly, cert'nly, cert'nly Lord!

Has your soul been redeemed? Cert'nly Lord!
Has your soul been redeemed? Cert'nly Lord!
Has your soul been redeemed? Cert'nly Lord!
Oh! Cert'nly, cert'nly, cert'nly Lord!

Have you been baptized? Cert'nly Lord!
Have you been baptized? Cert'nly Lord!
Have you been baptized? Cert'nly Lord!
Cert'nly, cert'nly, cert'nly Lord!

We have good religion, we've been baptized,
But has your name been recorded?
Cert'nly, cert'nly, cert'nly Lord!

SING ALLELUIA TO THE LORD 155

Unknown

Guys: **Sing Alleluia to the Lord**
Girls: *Sing Alleluia to the Lord*

Guys: **Sing Alleluia to the Lord**
Girls: *Sing Allelu-ia*

Guys: **Sing Alleluia, Sing Alleluia**
Girls: *Al-le-lu-ia*

Unison: **Sing Alleluia to the Lord.**

1. **Jesus is Lord of Heaven and Earth.**
2. **Jesus is King and Lord of all.**
3. **He's coming back to claim His own.**

INDEX

Music accompaniment not available for songs followed by **(L)**

Sea Festival

Young Life materials can be purchased at your local Christian Bookstore or you may order direct from:

Young Life National Services
P. O. Box 520
Colorado Springs, Colorado 80901
(303) 473-4262

	Price	Quantity	Amount
SING with Young Life (words and guitar chords)	$ 2.50		$
SING with Young Life (words, guitar chords, music)	$ 4.95		
SKITS Set (volumes 1 & 2)	$ 8.95		
SKITS Volume 1	$ 4.95		
SKITS Volume 2	$ 4.95		
GROW (three-year Studies in Basic Christianity)	$ 6.95		
COUNSELOR TRAINING SERIES	$29.95		
GET GROWIN' (booklet)	$ 1.25		
VAGLE'S RECORDING "I Bought My Wedding Dress at the Drugstore"	$ 6.95		
		Sub Total	
		3% State Tax (Colo. residents)	
		Handling Charge	$ 1.00
		Add 5% for shipping	
		TOTAL ENCLOSED	$

Make checks payable to
Young Life National Services.

Prices subject to change without notice.

Grow!

How to Study the Bible

Made to stimulate discussion. Includes leader's preface and extensive bibliography for further study. Written by Young Life's leaders, it's a three-year study in a 67-page looseleaf notebook. Covers Becoming a Christian, Living the Life, Relationships with Others, Knowing God's Will, Knowing Your Gifts, How to Study the Bible.

Retail – $6.95

GET GROWIN'

Our new booklet written with young Christians in mind! Excellent for small group or individual study. Written by a former Young Life staff person who has affected the lives of many new Christians with her inspirational teaching of scripture.

Retail $1.25

COUNSELOR TRAINING
Manuals and Cassette Tapes

SELF-AWARENESS AND SKILL TRAINING for counselors

PROBLEM SOLVING through personal planning

GOALS: organized steps in a purposeful Christian life

Utilizing COMMUNITY RESOURCES

Dr. Oraker, Director of Clinical Services at the Dale House, Colorado Springs, has served on the Young Life staff for ten years as a club leader, camp counselor, camp program director and area director. In 1970 he received his doctorate in clinical psychology from the Fuller Graduate School of Psychology, and received the seminary's award for the most outstanding contribution toward the integration of psychology and theology. He is a practicing psychologist with extensive experience in marriage, adolescent and family counseling.

A resource package for training counselors by Jim Oraker, Ph.D., Young Life's Clinical Psychologist. Consists of five manuals and five cassette tapes relating to the manuals. All in an attractive 8½ x 11 binder.

Retail $29.95

"Since training Christian outreach workers is felt to be our most significant contribution to the church, this will be the focus of this manual."

CASSETTE TAPES
personal growth material

The selection was assembled from a wide variety of Young Life events. There are tapes from staff conference speakers, sessions of training situations, of inspiration, motivation and Biblical interpretation. Many are by Young Life staff. Some are by those who have helped inspire and train Young Life staff. A series by Jim Rayburn, Young Life's founder, will give insight into the dynamic way God used this man to begin the Young Life outreach to kids.

Write for your free catalog!

A new recording by Fred and Anne Vagle

"I Bought My Wedding Dress at the Drugstore"

No musical group in Young Life has contributed any more fun, delight and satisfaction to so many than Fred and Anne Vagle. Their name is synonymous with the best of Young Life entertainment. Together they have entertained thousands at Young Life camps, events and banquets. They write most of what they sing and this, their first album, is something special, just as Fred and Anne are special to kids and adults all over the country. Their music seems to symbolize the Young Life style. It's warm, friendly, sincere, personal.

Retail $6.95

All kids everywhere love . . .

Skits

A new compilation of more than four hundred skits and ideas for youth groups. They've all been proven in Young Life clubs. Great ice breakers, involvement tools . . . just plain fun! SKITS tells how to do them, what props are needed. Many photographic illustrations.

Retail Volumes 1 & 2 – $4.95 each – 2-volume set $8.95.

CHORD CHART

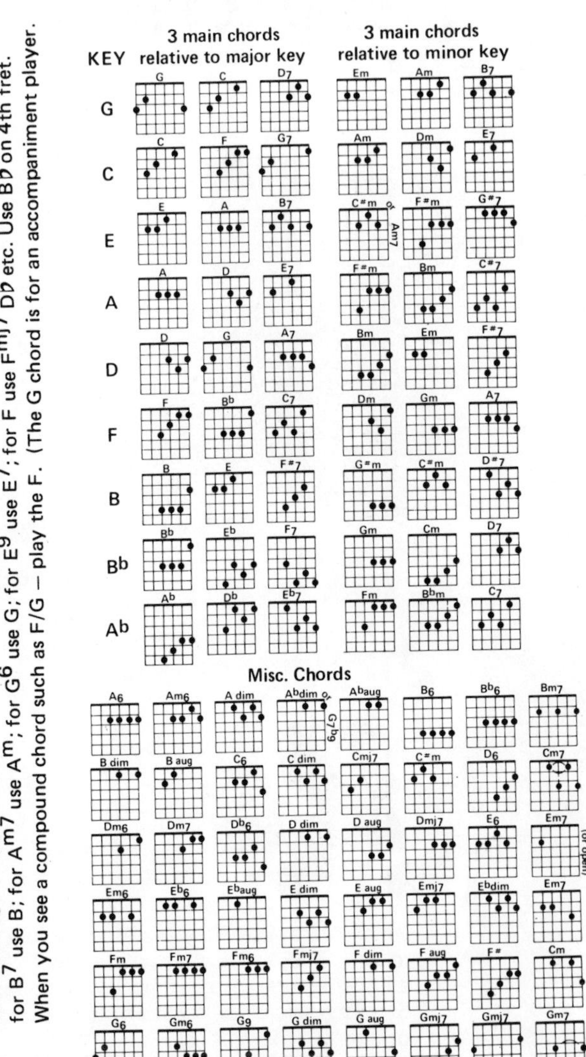

Note for beginning guitar players: You may simplify difficult chords in the following manner: for B^7 use B; for A^{m7} use A^m; for G^6 use G; for E^9 use E^7; for F use F^{mj7} D♭ etc. Use B♭ on 4th fret. When you see a compound chord such as F/G — play the F. (The G chord is for an accompaniment player.